Satan

The Hiss and Tell Memoirs

D0332648

Pan Books
London, Sydney and Auckland

Satan

The Hiss and Tell Memoirs

First published 1987 by Ebury Press

This edition published 1989 by Pan Books Ltd
Cavaye Place, London SW10 9PG

9 8 7 6 5 4 3 2 1

© Jeremy Pascall 1987

© Illustrations: Katherine Lamb 1987

ISBN 0 330 30973 0

Printed and bound in Great Britain by
Richard Clay Ltd, Bungay, Suffolk.

A MESSAGE FROM THE AUTHOR

IF YOU ARE TEMPTED TO STEAL THIS BOOK...
GO AHEAD!

Just pick it up, slip it into your pocket or bag and walk out of the shop.
Take it from a friend's shelf.
Or pretend to borrow it with no intention of returning it.

Go on, do it! Be a devil!*

* The publishers would like to dissociate themselves from this flagrant incitement to theft. In fact, the publishers would like to dissociate themselves from everything contained in this book. We only agreed to publish it because we felt that, in a free society, even The Author has a right to put his point of view, however dishonest, twisted and perverse.
And because we hope to make lots and lots of lovely lucre.

DEDICATION

This book is dedicated to Pride, Anger, Envy, Lust,
Gluttony, Greed and Sloth.
And so am I.
Why not join me and indulge in the
Seven Delightful Sins?
Think of the fun we could have together!*

* Discover the joy of the Eighth Delightful Sin later in the book!

PUBLISHER'S WARNING

While we took every effort to check the facts in this book, it must be remembered that The Author is the most accomplished liar in the history of the universe.

Nothing contained in this book should be believed.

Except this statement.

And, frankly, even this is not entirely true because we made very little effort to check the facts. Mainly because the first editor who worked with The Author disappeared under unusual and suspicious circumstances and was last seen dancing stark naked on Salisbury Plain, sacrificing a chicken by biting its head off.

And the second editor...well, suffice it to say that the second editor who had the temerity to question The Author on the veracity of the text suddenly changed his job. And his form. Having no vacancies in the company for a goat, however talented, we reluctantly let him go. But not, sadly, before he had eaten part of the manuscript and most of the Managing Director's furniture.

The third and last editor decided, wisely in our opinion, not to challenge The Author on any of his so-called facts. She struck up a close working relationship with The Author and, as a result, is alive and well in the Seychelles, living very comfortably on the £500,000 she embezzled from this company.

BY THE SAME AUTHOR

'Arson for Profit and Pleasure'

'The Good Hell Guide'

'Incest – Fun for all the Family'

'Hell's Kitchen – 100 Tempting Barbecue Dishes'
(including Devilled Crab, Angels on Horseback –
made with real angels and horses – and Soul,
fried, grilled and meunière)

'The Living Dead – Biographies of Six Famous
Belgians' (Well, all right, Three Quite Well
Known Belgians)

'The Boy's Big Book of Torture'

'The Girl's Big Book of Bonking'

'The Joy of Sin'

'The Joy of Goats'

'The Country Diary of an Edwardian Ladykiller'

'My Animals and Other Family'

'Paradise Lost – What Really Happened in Heaven'

'Paradise Mislaid – What Really Happened
to Atlantis'

'Work for Idle Hands – A Manual
of Black Arts and Crafts'

(All recommended by *Witch* Magazine.)

Sintroduction

REETINGS!

Allow me to introduce myself. I am Satan. Or, if you prefer, The Devil, Lucifer, The Prince of Darkness, The Evil One, The Serpent, Beezlebub, Mephistopheles, Old Nick ...I answer to all these. Although I'm not too happy about the last. Nick, I may be, but old? I'm considerably younger than Him Upstairs. Compared to The Great Fraud, as I call Him, I'm a teenager. All right, I've been around a long time but I don't consider myself elderly. What I say is, you're as old as you feel; or as old as the woman you feel! (Or the man or goat you feel. I think it's silly to be prejudiced about these matters. My philosophy is: don't knock it until you've tried it. Or, to put it another way, suck it and see. And, of course, vice versa.)

I really do object to being depicted as old. How many other men of my age regularly perform fifteen despicable acts, destroy the careers of six public figures, corrupt a dozen Catholic priests and fornicate with a variety of living creatures each and every day? And all before breakfast!

11

I have my pride, you know. In fact, Pride is my favourite sin. All right, it's not as much fun as Lust or Gluttony or Greed but, of course, I take enormous pride in my lustfulness and nobody, but nobody, is as gluttonous as me. However, when it comes to Greed I have to acknowledge that lawyers may have the edge.

But I digress. It's one of my little failings, one of my many little failings along with unpunctuality, untidiness, meanness and rampant kleptomania. Of course, I also have many big failings – like sexual depravity, genocide and not using a hankie when I sneeze – which you'll learn about in due course.

To return to my subject: you probably know me best as Satan. But my real name is Kevin.

Kevin! Yes, that's my Chris...ooops! nearly had to wash my mouth with soap and brimstone...my forename. Can't stand it myself, I'd have preferred something with a bit more nobility about it. Typical, isn't it, that when G** – I can't even bring myself to type His name – when The Great Fraud, was handing out names to His other archangels, they were called Gabriel, Raphael, Uriel and Zadkiel, but not me. I got Kevin. Which just goes to prove He never liked me. I sometimes wonder what would have happened if He'd called me something decent like Azrael. Perhaps I wouldn't have had such a chip on my shoulder and things would have turned out differently. Maybe I'd have stayed in Heaven and helped Him out, doing odd jobs like polishing halos, tuning harps and clipping the wings of cherubim who tried to fly before they could walk. How boring! I've no regrets about the existence I've led, so much more fun than Heaven. Mind you, even Belgium is more fun than Heaven. Or would be, if it didn't have so many Belgians.

So now you know my real name and the first of my big secrets is out – just one of the many I will reveal in these pages.

I know some people are surprised that I've taken so long to write my memoirs. There are many reasons for this, not least the fact that I've been waiting for a publisher to come up with enough lucre. Of course, over the eons others have tried to persuade me to jot down my life story and I've frequently been tempted. But, you see, I'm so easily tempted. In fact, as I once rather wittily commented, I can resist anything except temptation![1]

Being so prone to temptation, I've always signed the contract, taken the lucre and run off with it without writing a word. Serves them right for trusting me and anyway what can they do about it? Sue me? It would never stand up in court, especially as most of the lawyers in the world work for me – you've heard of devil's advocates, haven't you? I really admire lawyers, brilliant people who lie, cheat and steal you blind and it's all absolutely legal! They're people after my own heart and, indeed, wallet. What a blow for Him Upstairs! The Great Fraud may have formulated the laws, but the people who bend, twist and pervert them are good chums of mine. I've reserved a very special place in Hell for lawyers.

The reason that I'm finally dipping my nib in vitriol and putting pen to paper is that at last someone has come up with enough incentive for me to do it. True, there was a problem when I told the publishers that I wanted to be paid in either (i) their souls or (ii) virgins. Caused a lot of consternation because it seems that most publishers have already sold the first and none of the second could be found working in their trade. In the end I settled for truck-loads of lucre.[2]

Not that I need the lucre, you understand. I'm probably the richest being in history. Compared to me, your average billionaire is a beggar and I made J. Paul Getty look like a pauper. And, indeed, I made him look like a porpoise. Didn't you ever wonder why he was so glum? People used to comment that he had all that money and yet he looked as miserable as

1. *Publisher's note:* Most sources ascribe that remark to Oscar Wilde. It would seem that The Author has plagiarized this line but, as he points out, 'Not for nothing am I known as The Bubonic Plagiarist! I only steal from the best. Unless I'm getting new ideas for wickedness and then I only steal from the very worst.'

2. The publishers would like to point out that we are paying The Author the usual fee for writing this book plus, of course, his royalties. Or, rather, Satanies. And we'd further like to add that in the matter of greed, unscrupulousness and treachery, The Author is no worse than the average literary agent. In fact, he has rather more integrity than most.

sin. I take exception to that. I'm here to tell you that sin isn't miserable, it's deliciously pleasurable.

The trouble with Getty was that he didn't know how to enjoy his money and when I offered him some tips – like using it to destabilize the economies of Third World countries – he spurned me. So in revenge I gave him the face of a fish. (Him Upstairs later stole this idea and used it on Andrew Lloyd Webber. The reason the poor blighter looks like he does is because he failed to pay The Great Fraud His deities for 'Jesus Christ Superstar'. You know, He has a vicious streak that even I have to admire, grudgingly.)

But even being so rich doesn't mean that I don't want more lucre. I want it all! Never believe people when they tell you that money doesn't buy you happiness, that's just a rumour put around by the wonderfully and disgustingly wealthy to stop the rest of you getting your hands on their's. Sadly, however, it is true that you can't take it with you, otherwise I'd have had all the lovely lucre they brought down when they joined me in Hades. (Incidentally, I've disproved that non-sense put about by Him Upstairs when He said that a rich man can't pass through the eye of a needle. Of course he can. If you chop him up into little pieces – preferably while he's still alive – put him in a blender, squish him round until he's liquefied and then dribble him through the eye, drop by drop. A most enjoyable experiment!)[3]

Despite my enormous and insatiable greed, the lucre is not the main reason I've consented to write these memoirs. Frankly, during the last few years my company, Hades p.l.c., has suffered a few setbacks. For some reason there's been a nasty outbreak of piety in the world. This, of course, may just be the usual pendulum of trade. We did particularly well in the 'sixties and 'seventies – recruitment flourished with

3. When we pointed out to The Author that the Biblical text tells us that it is easier for a camel to pass through the eye of a needle than for a rich man to enter Heaven, he said, 'I've only read The Bible once and that was to check for any loopholes. And anyway, squishing a camel is not nearly as much fun as liquefying a bloated capitalist.' The publishers would like to warn young readers not to attempt this experiment for themselves as it is cruel, perverted and may cause irreparable damage to your mother's food blender.

enormously encouraging increases among the young and we ruthlessly exploited the growth area of capturing the souls of such trendy hedonists as actors and, particularly, rock stars who were falling into our hands at a tremendous rate. Oh, for those heady days of sex and drugs and rock and roll and sex and drugs and more sex! There was a time when you could hardly move down here without rubbing shoulders (and other far more interesting parts of the anatomy) with some pop superstar.

But since 1980 business hasn't been so good. Despite my worst efforts I've found that more and more people have been turning to the opposition, buying what The Great Fraud calls His 'fire insurance' – sign up with Him and He'll guarantee you won't enjoy the many and varied benefits of my own organization.

My firm's motto has always been 'Live Now, Pay Later', but His marketing boys have come up with a new campaign around the slogan 'Pray Now, Live For Ever' which, to my surprise and disappointment, has proved remarkably success-ful. Let's be hone...I mean, let's face it, we were caught unawares by the sheer number of Born Again Christians. In fact, it seems that there's one Born Again every minute, and to try to stem the flow I've decided to address you directly, to tell my story, to show you where you're going right and how much more pleasure you'll get if you go wrong.

So, read this book and enjoy it. And if at the end of it you don't want to follow me down the primrose path to eternal wickedness, let me just say: Have a lousy day. And remember what happend to the *Titanic*. That taught them to refuse me a free first-class cabin!

You know, I'm often accused of being a bad loser. And it's true. But to be fair, I'm also a very bad winner.

Satan

Chapter Twelve[4]
Not Quite The Beginning

I am the most maligned being in history and, indeed, in prehistory given that I was around long before you shambling anthropoids first set your stumbling feet on The Earth. It's hard to believe, but The Great Fraud is actually proud of creating you ramshackle creatures! I mean, look at you! Pathetic, stringy things without a decent pair of horns or even a tail. Mind you, He did create you on the sixth day, so I suppose He must have run out of inspiration, not to mention spare parts which probably explains why you look like you were hastily and carelessly flung together from the left-over bits of other animals.

Still, I was pleased enough to see some human life, however inadequate. Don't forget that I was about my devilishly devious work eons before Adam and Eve first saw the light of day. And very welcome they were, at least to me, because, let's face it, before them there was very little fun for a Satanic being. How would you like to waste your time, charm and

---

4. This is, of course, Chapter One. The author can't resist exaggerating.

seductive talents trying to tempt rocks into the ways of wickedness? Or persuading lumps of wood to indulge in rampant sexual orgies? So, you see, Adam and Eve were literally Heaven-sent for me. But I digress again, I'll get around to the tru...no, I have trouble with that word too... the *real* story of Adam and Eve in my own bad time.

To return to the subject: ever since I pulled off my first successful temptation in the Garden of Eden, I have been reviled and vilified, pilloried and libelled; every misfortune, disaster and catastrophe has been blamed on me. I've been accused of everything from the destruction of Pompeii to causing the First World War.[5] Of every evil from the introduction of murder to the invention of nylon tights.

While I'm prepared to proudly admit my involvement in the first three, I can't accept the blame for tights; they were the creation of a deeply puritanical mind and have probably done more to set back my campaign for unbridled lust than anything since the chastity belt. That, at least, had a profitable spin-off for me; namely, a huge increase in professional lock-pickers. Although, of course, there were always those who wanted to take a short cut; I'm thinking of a passionate young swain called Rufus the Dickhead who decided to free his loved one from her confinement by attaching a charge of dynamite to her iron girdle. Gave her a terrific bang, but he had trouble explaining to her husband when he returned from the Crusades how she came to be buried in a very small envelope. In fact, he completely failed to come up with a convincing story. Unfortunately for him, the husband was a man of violent temper which explains how the swain subsequently became known as Rufus the Dickless.

There I go, digressing again. What I'm saying is that I've been getting a bad press since time immemorial and, of course, in *Time Immemorial*, the magazine for immortals, which has named me as its 'Evil Bastard of the Year' for 7,237,961,548 years running. I ask you, has any being ever had a worse reputation?

---

5. What a brilliant coup World War One was! Imagine me persuading two super-powers like Britain and Germany to plunge the Earth into global conflict. And all over Belgium!

So, let's get one thing straight from the start: I love it! I revel in each and every slur. The more I'm accused, the more I enjoy it. You should see my scrapbooks – volume after volume of stories about me and not one good word to be found in my favour! In spare moments, when I'm not trying to lead you all towards Armageddon, I drool over the billions of reports of my despicable deeds! Do you realize that when asked, ninety out of a hundred ordinary mass murderers in the street claimed that I was their inspiration! Very flattering. The remaining ten said they had been motivated after hearing the voice of Him Upstairs ordering them to kill in His name. Gullible fools! Do they really think He'd talk to them? He's so high and mighty, He barely deigns to pass the time of day with His saints. And don't they realize that ventriloquism is one of my many talents!

Oh, I simply love being me, I wouldn't change myself for all the tea in China. Hang on, though...that's rather tempting. If you were also to throw in all the souls in China, we might have a deal. Although, of course, I'd instantly renege on it.

Yes, I *adore* being evil. Wickedness is so much more fun than piety. I've spent almost my entire existence enjoying every sin and transgression you can imagine and many hundreds more that your minuscule minds aren't capable of imagining. I've indulged myself in the pursuit of pleasure and wallowed in every physical gratification. There is nothing I haven't done, no sexual depravity I haven't experienced. (How many of you can boast of enjoying an active sexual relationship with a duckbilled platypus? And a homosexual relationship at that? Quite pleasurable it was too. But not as truly satisfying as doing something unspeakably depraved with a dead warthog. But enough of these nostalgic reminiscences about my past loves. Sometimes I think that I'm just a silly, sentimental old romantic.)

I've relished every moment of my misspent existence. And, being a generous man, I've always been willing to share my life-style with you. Yes, YOU. For example, why don't you put this book down for a moment and do something really naughty? Go on! It doesn't *have* to be arson or blood-letting (great fun in themselves, but they make a terrible mess of the carpet), it could be something simple to start with, like scoffing a whole box of chocolates, drinking another bottle of wine or whipping your gerbil with barbed wire. Whatever it is, do it! You'll feel better for it afterwards. Believe me. Would I lie to you?[6]

The point I'm making is that you shouldn't believe everything you read about me. I'm not as bad as I'm made out to be. I'm much, much worse. I'm so irredeemably wicked that I make Adolf Hitler look like Mother Teresa.

That's how truly, utterly evil I am and the question many people ask is: have I always been evil? Was I created evil? Or did I just practise long and hard? To answer that I'll have to go right back to The Beginning...

---

6. Yes, of course, I would lie to you. It's my business, my craft, my art and my pleasure. But on the other hand, I'm such a practised liar that you can never be sure that I'm not lying when I say that I'd lie to you. The trouble is that when I say I'm lying to you, I am, in fact, telling the truth. But as I'm incapable of telling the truth, I must be lying. Oh, what intricate webs of deception I weave! Sometimes I even confuse myself.

Chapter Seven[7]
The Beginning

n the beginning was the Word and the Word was 'w********k' which is the rudest word in the whole universe. It is so rude that grown men have been known to spontaneously combust just at the sound of it. And grown women have been known to commit acts of gross sexual abandon with Christmas trees. That's how rude it is. And I was the very first person ever to utter the word. In fact, it was the first word I ever spoke when still just a seraphim and only knee high to a cockroach.[8]

7. This is, of course, Chapter Two. The Author is lying in an attempt to cause confusion.

8. For obvious reasons we are not able to print the word in full. The only time it has been written, in a medieval manuscript, was by a monk who was inscribing it on to parchment. As soon as he penned the last letter, his head exploded. The precise meaning of the word is unclear as it has never appeared in a dictionary. But we believe that a rough definition is: 'to derive sexual stimulation by using a porcupine as a suppository.' We would like to warn any children not to attempt this as it stunts the growth, causes blindness and may lead to madness. Apart from these effects on the porcupine, it won't do you any good either.

This, of course, was long, long before your Earth was created, when the universe was just a black void waiting to be filled. All that existed in those far-off days was Heaven. Well, The Great Fraud called it Heaven but the rest of us didn't think much of it. A dreary place, not much better than a shack, painted ditchwater brown and sludge green. We often used to complain about it, especially the plumbing which left a lot to be desired, like pipes, running water and a toilet seat. But The Great Fraud said it was Paradise compared to everything else, which was accurate considering there wasn't anything else.

In those dull days there was just Him Upstairs and His few archangels – Gabriel, Raphael, Uriel, Zadkiel and me, Tracie.[9]

He'd created us when He became bored whizzing about the utterly empty universe looking in vain for some place to hang out on a Saturday night where He could have a couple of beers, play a game of pool and listen to His favourite hymns on the jukebox. He decided He needed some companions with whom to share the so-called delights of Heaven, to be His disciples and pupils and to do the washing up.

We were the first beings He created and, though I say it myself, we were a damn fine looking bunch of ethereals. In our halos, enormous wings and spotless white frocks we positively glowed, so you can understand that we didn't take kindly to living in a slum. I mean, no sooner had you put on a clean frock in the morning and stepped outside than it was grubby and, remember, this was long before a really reliable biological washing powder came on the market.

Now, I'm not one to gossip. Well, of course, I *am* one to gossip, I mean who do you think put around the rumour about St Cecilia using a Great Dane as a vibro-massager? (Not to

9. All right, I lied when I said my name was Kevin, I was too embarrassed to reveal that I started my existence as Tracie. What sort of name is that? Especially for a boy? I still believe that He called me it out of spite. I protested to Him about it and pleaded with Him to change it, which reluctantly He did. Which is how I spent the next three millennia answering to the name of Rover.

No wonder I turned out as I did. You know what they say, give a god a bad name…

mention a Terrific Swede and a Really Buttock-Clenchingly Fantastic Norwegian.) And being one to gossip, I ask you, what sort of Supreme Being dresses His male archangels in frocks? Okay, so He called them kaftans, but does that explain why He insisted that we wore frou-frou bras, lace basques, suspender belts and silk stockings underneath them? I tell you, He's one weird old man. Look at the facts – has He ever been seen out with a woman? Never! Always going around with a bunch of men. And the only time He felt the need to procreate Himself, what happened? He got The Holy Ghost to do it for Him. I leave you to draw your own conclusions.

What else can I tell you about Heaven? The clothes were suspect, the plumbing was primitive, the accommodation was awful and the food was worse. We survived on a staple diet of nectar and ambrosia which have been greatly over-rated by scholars and poets who never had to eat the stuff. Nectar resembles mud-flavoured yogurt while ambrosia has the look and consistency of blotting paper but, sadly, doesn't taste half as nice. One of my first clashes with Him was about the menu.

When I complained, all He could say was: 'You've got ambrosia to eat and nectar to drink. What else do you want?'

So I said, 'What else have You got?'

'Nothing,' He said.

'Nothing? Why not?'

'Because there isn't anything else.'

'Well,' I said, 'why don't You create something?'

'Like what?'

'Like caviar,' I suggested.

'Caviar?' He boomed. 'What's caviar?'

'I don't know, but it's a nice word. Why don't you create something caviar-ish?'

'Like what?' He asked.

'I don't know. Like fishes' eggs, maybe?'

'You know, Rover,' He said. 'Sometimes you really disgust me. What sort of pervert would want to eat fishes' eggs?'

I explained it was just an idea off the top of my halo but He wouldn't have any of it. 'And furthermore,' He continued, 'what on Heaven are fishes?'

There He had me. 'I don't know what they are. I just thought of a word. "Fish", it sounds like something we could eat, so why don't You, in Your infinite omnipotence which You are constantly boasting about, create "fish" which we could eat? I mean, it doesn't *have* to be "fish", it could be… well, to pull another word out of the air…it could be "sofa". I don't care what it's called so long as it isn't nectar or bloody ambrosia.'

'Rover,' He shouted, 'I would remind you that I am God Almighty, Lord of the Universe, The Supreme Being and not a short-order cook.'

'All right,' I said, 'keep Your hair on.'

Now, that's where I got Him. He's very sensitive to any references about His hair. Or, rather, lack of it. What you don't realize is that He's completely bald. I expect you've seen all those portraits of Him with His long flowing locks – well, they're a con. What you don't know is He's wearing a wig. And a very unconvincing one. I mean, who does He think He's fooling with a snowy white beard and bright ginger hair? He really does look ludicrous. What a stroke I pulled when I persuaded Him to wear it!

Anyway, I eventually managed to goad Him into coming up with some alternative food. And the next day we all tucked into His latest creation – sand-flavoured pot noodles.

When we'd finished the meal, He said, 'So, what do you think of it?'

And Gabriel, being a grovelling little crawler, said, 'Verily, it is a feast and a banquet. Never has anyone dined on such exquisite fare.'

And Raphael, Uriel and Zadkiel – fearing for their jobs – all concurred. 'Verily, You have created the food of the Gods.'

And The Great Fraud turned to me and said, 'And what do you think, Rover?'

And I said, 'I think Verily is a stupid name for The Supreme Being and You should change it immediately. And while You're about it, You can change my name too.'

He waxed wrathful at this, saying, 'Verily is not My name!'

And the others said, 'Verily, Verily is *not* His name. Verily is a word we made up while you were washing your frock. It means "truly".'

And I thought that was typical of them, making up words behind my back just so they could win at Scrabble. But I said nothing, preferring to bide my time and plan my revenge.

Seeing my silence, The Great Fraud said, 'Stop sulking. If you don't like being called Rover, what name would you like?'

'I don't know. One like the others have. Something classy that ends in "iel".'

He thought for a moment and said, 'Very well. Let it be known that from this day hence Rover will be called Muriel.'

The others all laughed because in those days, when we were still making up names for things, 'Muriel' meant 'lavatory brush'. But I held my peace, knowing my time would come.

'So, Muriel,' said He, 'what do you think of my sand-flavoured pot noodles? Were they not delicious?'

'They were not delicious. They tasted like the inside of Gabriel's posing pouch.'

This caused great perturbation – especially to Gabriel who thought that none of us knew how he spent his evenings, standing in front of the mirror wearing nothing but his gold lamé pouch, flexing his muscles and saying, 'My but you're a good-looking hunk of angel!'

He and the others all shouted, 'Oh, Lord, do not listen to him. Believe us, Your sand-flavoured pot noodles are the greatest thing since sliced...since sliced whatjamacallit? Oooh, what was the name of that sliced thing You created the day before yesterday?'

And He said, 'Manure.'

And they all carolled, 'Verily, they are the greatest thing since sliced manure! And we'd like second helpings!'

He turned to me again, 'See, Muriel, everyone else likes My pot noodles.'

To which I replied, 'You may be The Lord of All Creation, The Supreme and Omnipotent Being, but you're a lousy cook. Personally, I'd prefer to eat my own intestines.'

And he glowered at me and spake. And when He spake, His voice was as thunder.

'I should have known it from the moment I created you, you're a trouble-maker.'

And the others all chorused: 'Yes! Muriel is a trouble-maker! Muriel is a trouble-maker!'

And then they said, 'What's "trouble"? Can you eat it? If so, will you make us some, Muriel?'

I replied, 'I don't know what "trouble" is, but when I find out I promise I'll make plenty of it for you.'

They all shouted 'Oh! Goody!'

But Himself spake not a word. He just glared, frowning furiously at me under His ginger wig.

'Oh, w********k it!,' I thought to myself, 'Why didn't I keep my mouth shut?'

And that was The End of The Beginning of The Beginning.

Chapter Thirteen[10]

The Middle of The Beginning

The next day we all sat down to our meal again. And after Himself had said grace – 'For what I am about to provide, may you all be truly grateful' – He said, 'I have made an important decision. I have decided that there will be no repeat of what happened yesterday. In future there will be no more arguments between us. Understand, Muriel?'

And I said, 'What happened yesterday was not an argument.'

And He said, 'Yes, it was!'

'No, it wasn't!'

'Was, too!'

'Wasn't!'

---

10. This is, of course, Chapter Three. Originally, The Author wanted every chapter to be Thirteen, 'because it's my favourite number, unlucky for most which makes it very lucky for me. My second favourite number is 666 – the number of The Beast. Whenever I need something beastly done, I dial 666 and it comes running to do my diabolic bidding.'

'Was! Was! WAS!'

And I said, 'Look, what we had yesterday was a heated exchange of views in which we offered our opinions fully and frankly. What we're doing now is having an argument.'

'This is *not* an argument!'

'Yes it is!'

'No, it isn't!'

And I said, 'Yes it is, but there's no use arguing about it.'

'I am NOT arguing!'

'Yes, You are!'

'No I am NOT!'

'All right,' I said, 'Have it Your own way. But there's no point in getting hoity-toity just because You can't admit You're wrong.'

And He waxed wrathful again and declared, 'I am NEVER wrong! It is not possible for Me to be wrong, I am God Almighty, The Supreme and Perfect Being. I am utterly infallible. And if you don't shut up, I'll turn you into a toad. How would you like that?'

And I said, 'I'm not sure. What's a toad?'

'A toad?' He said.

'Yes, as You are The Supreme and Perfect Being, who can't get anything wrong, just tell me what a toad is.'

'Well, um, it's a large four-legged animal with a flowing mane and a long swishy tail. So there! Now, that's enough of that, let's eat!'

'Hear! Hear!,' said Gabriel, 'I'm starving!'

And the others agreed, saying, 'We're so hungry we could eat a toad!'

Himself served up the food. This time, instead of the miserable little portions we usually got, the table groaned under a huge dish covered with an enormous silver dome. Before He whipped off the dome, He said, 'This is My latest culinary masterpiece!' And with a flourish He revealed it to us.

We looked at it in awed silence, then we sniffed the aroma steaming off it and we prodded it with our forks. Truly we had seen nothing to compare with it. Eventually Gabriel broke the expectant hush.

'It's certainly very large.'

'Very large,' agreed Raphael.

'Now,' said Uriel, 'if I was asked for just one word to describe it, that word would, without any doubt, be "large".'

'Extraordinary you should say that,' chipped in Zadkiel, 'because, believe it or not, the first word that sprang to my mind when I saw it was "large".'

'Is that all you've got to say?' asked Himself.

'Well,' said Gabriel, 'we haven't actually tried it yet. Perhaps when we've tasted it we'll be able to say something else.'

So Himself carved us each a slice and placed it before us and one by one we tasted it.

'Well?' He demanded.

Again Gabriel was the first to speak. 'I can say without a shadow of doubt that in all my experience this is absolutely and unequivocally the largest thing I've ever eaten.'

'Amazingly, incredibly and extraordinarily large!' agreed the rest.

'Yes, yes,' said Himself, 'but what do you think of the flavour?'

'The flavour?' said Gabriel. 'Ah! The flavour! How can I describe it? Of course, I'm not an expert, but I'd say that it has an extremely large flavour.'

'Exactly!,' the others chimed in. 'It has an extraordinarily and uniquely large flavour. We couldn't have put it better ourselves!'

Himself turned to me, saying, 'You've been very quiet, Muriel. What have you got to say about My latest creation? Would you describe it as "large"?'

'Well, it is indubitably large but that's not the word I'd use to describe the flavour.'

'And what word would you use?'

'"Disgusting". It tastes stomach-churningly, gut-wrenchingly disgusting. What is it?'

'It's something you suggested yesterday. It's "sofa". And if you don't like it, you know where you can stick it!'

I took Him at His word. Which is how the 'sofa' came to be stuck in the corner of the room until someone could think of a use for it. I can't exactly remember who came up with the idea of a purpose for left-over 'sofa' but, typically, Himself claimed the credit, as He did for all good ideas. However, after it had stood in the corner for a couple of thousand years, somebody had the bright idea of using it as a place to lose things. For example, if one of us couldn't find our halo the others would say: 'I bet it's behind the "sofa".' Or 'Have you looked under the "sofa"?' Or, alternatively, 'I wouldn't be the slightest bit surprised if it hasn't fallen down the side of the "sofa".' So we'd go and look. And nine times out of ten we would discover the missing object behind, under or in the 'sofa'. Yes, the perfect function of a sofa was as a handy place to lose things.

One day, Gabriel came into the room, exhausted after his weight-training and, instead of hovering just above the ground, cooling himself off in the breeze from his wings, he casually slumped on to the 'sofa'. And, after a moment, he leapt into the air shouting, 'Eureka!'

We all turned to him in amazement and said, 'What does "eureka" mean?'

To which he replied, 'It means, "Bloody Norah, I've got a castor up my bum! And it isn't half painful".'

After that we steered well clear of the 'sofa' until, finally, we decided to throw it out. We put it in the back yard, but this time with the castors on the ground instead of sticking up in the air. And, looking at it, Gabriel said, 'I think I've found a better use for the "sofa".'

'Really?' we replied. 'What use?'

'Well, I've been looking at it very carefully. And judging from the size and shape and contours of it, it occurred to me that this "sofa" would make an absolutely perfect bonfire.'

So we set fire to it.

And when it had finished burning, Raphael picked up one of the embers saying, 'It looks good.' And he sniffed it, saying, 'By golly, it smells good.' And he licked it, saying, 'Mmmmm! It tastes good! It's really delicious! You know what?'

And I said, 'Don't tell me. The daft old so-and-so under-cooked it.'

The next thing I knew, the ground was shaking and there was the sound of thunder and through the thunder came the voice of Himself, saying:

'I heard that, Muriel!
And I've half a mind...'

Boasting again, I thought.

'And I also read that thought! Any more of your insolence and I will turn you into a toad.'

I was tired of His niggling, so I said, 'It can't be any worse than hanging around here all day, eating terrible food and entertaining myself by looking for things behind the "sofa". So go ahead, turn me into a toad.'

And Himself said, 'No. Not today.'

'Why not?'

'I don't feel like it.'

'You mean, You *can't* turn me into a toad.'

'Of course, I can. I am God Almighty, The Supreme and...'

'Omnipotent Being. Yes, I know all that. Go on, if You're so powerful, turn me into a toad.'

'Well, I would, but I've got a headache.'

And to demonstrate it, He ran His hand over His fevered knee and limped off to His bed.

Gabriel watched Him hobbling away and said, 'Verily, The Lord does move in mysterious ways.'

'Yea,' said the others. 'Verily, He does.'

I said nothing, but thought, how can I respect a Being who doesn't know His head from His knee? One day there are going to be some changes around here.

And that was The End of The Middle of The Beginning.

Chapter Four-ish

A Little Bit After The End of The Middle of The Beginning

ou might find it difficult to believe that the emnity between Himself and me started with such seeming trivialities as the names He gave me and the food He forced us to eat.[11]

But that just goes to show the pettiness of the so-called Supreme Being. There was absolutely no reason why He shouldn't have given me a suitably Biblical name. It was obvious that He took against me from the start just because I was different from the rest of the archangels. It was hardly my fault that while Gabriel, Raphael, Uriel and Zadkiel all had lustrous golden wings, mine were a rather curious sort of tartan, comprising vibrant green and a shade of orange that some might describe as 'electric' but which I always considered to be on the vulgar side of garish. I didn't choose the

---

11. *Publisher's note:* Yes, we do find it difficult to believe. In fact, we find it impossible. Just thought we'd mention that in case God is as petty as The Author claims and takes His revenge by doing something nasty, like turning us into one of the lower forms of pond life. Or, if He's feeling particularly vindictive, Belgians.

blasted things, He gave them to me and I can only conclude that in addition to being totally bald, He was also colour-blind.

Apart from these bloody great plaid things flapping round my back and making it incredibly difficult to sit down without creasing them — and sitting on your own wings really bring tears to your eyes, let me tell you; almost as bad as having a castor up your bum — I was different in other respects to the rest of the archangels.

For a start, they were all blond, while my hair was jet black, and this caused me no end of problems when I was a cherubim. The others teased me mercilessly, calling me names and doubting my paternity, which was ridiculous because as there was only Himself in the whole universe it rather narrowed down the list of possible candidates.

As I grew from cherubim to seraphim to archangelhood, I became increasingly self-conscious about my black hair and spent hours in the bathroom with bottles of peroxide trying to make myself look like the others. Even when I became a platinum blond, Gabriel never lost the opportunity to humiliate me by saying things like, 'Muriel, have you ever thought of painting your halo to match your wings? Oh, and by the way, your roots are showing.'

Himself was no better. As I grew up He never really forgave me for being taller than Him. In fact, all the archangels were taller than Him, standing as He did only five feet two inches even when wearing three pairs of His thickest socks. He couldn't bear the fact that the so-called Supreme Being had to look up to others but forgave Gabriel and the rest because they always stooped in His presence. However, being the tallest of all and refusing to stoop for anyone, I still towered above Him even when He was standing on the box He carried everywhere. This drove Him into a rage and eventually He took to wearing sandals with seven-inch platform heels. This made Him slightly happier until the day He tripped, fell off His shoes and hit the ground with a sickening crunch. Nothing was hurt but His pride, He didn't take kindly to having to crawl under the 'sofa' in order to retrieve His wig and, of course, He had to have someone to blame. Guess who? Most unfair. It was His own fault. If He's omniscient He should have known my foot was, by pure accident, sticking out in His path.

He is, as has often been pointed out, a jealous God and the way He got His revenge was by giving me stupid names.

As for the food: you must understand that in the early eons of Heaven there really wasn't anything to do, so all we had to look forward to were our meals. There was no entertainment, except for Raphael and his harp which he played every evening.

Each night, after yet another appalling meal, we'd all sit around this crummy shack, bored out of our minds, trying to while away the hours before bed.

Gabriel would polish his halo until he could see his own face in it and then he'd gaze lovingly at his reflection for hours, muttering, 'Who's a pretty angel, then?' Zadkiel would preen his wings incessantly, teasing them this way and that, saying, 'What do you think? Am I moulting or not? I'm almost certain that this feather is coming loose. I do hope it's not going to drop out. There's nothing worse than bedraggled plumage, makes one feel such a fright.'

Uriel would crawl around and under the 'sofa', hoping that something had been lost so he could shout, 'Look what I've just found! And you'll never guess where I found it!' To which the others would reply, 'Oh! Don't tell us! It wasn't under the "sofa", was it?'

I would just sit there, belching quietly, and wishing that the so-called Supreme Being had been omnipotent enough to create a cure for indigestion.

In the midst of this riveting hurly-burly Himself would boom: 'So! What shall we do this evening?'

We'd all say 'Ummm...er...That's a tough one. Let's have a long, hard think.'

Then He'd bellow, 'Hands up all those in favour of Raphael giving us a tune on his harp.'

All the others would shout: 'What a spiffing idea! Just what I fancy! Gosh You *are* clever! I wish I'd thought of that!'

And Raphael would go coy, 'Oh, you don't *really* want me to play my harp again.'

'Oh, yes, we do, Raphael! Honest!'

'Well, if you insist, but I'm terribly out of practice. I haven't even plucked a string since...oooh...it must have been last night. But here goes...'

He'd reach for his harp, run his fingers over the strings and say, 'What would you like me to play?'

To which Himself would reply, 'I don't know about anyone else, but what I'd really like to hear is something that praises My name.'

'Ooooh, yes!' they'd all chorus. 'What we'd really like to hear is something that praises Your name, too!'

And Raphael would say, 'What a truly extraordinary co-incidence! Because just this afternoon I wrote a little number that just happens to be called "Let's All Praise His Name" and it goes something like this...'

It always went exactly like...

Let's all praise His name!
Let's all praise His name!
Why don't we all join in and praise His name?
Yes, praise His name
Oh! praise His name
There really is nothing better in all of Heaven than
Praising His name!
So, let's all praise His name!

Then Raphael would insist that we all joined in the chorus:

Praise His name!
Praise His name!
Praise His name!
Praise His name!

Which was followed by the second verse:

Let's all praise His name!
Let's all praise His name!
Why don't we all join in and praise His name?
Yes, praise His name
Oh! praise His name
There really is nothing better in all of Heaven than
Praising His name!
So, let's all praise His name!

And when it was eventually finished, four hundred and

seventy verses later, Himself would say: 'Let's hear that one more time because I don't know what anyone else thinks but in My humble opinion – an opinion as humble as the Perfect and Supreme Being can manage – that was the very best song praising My name I've ever heard.'

And the others would all applaud and shout, 'Yes! Even better than the one last night, which we thought could not be improved. Raphael has done it again!'

And Raphael would blush and say, 'No, really, it wasn't *that* good. It still needs a lot of work. For instance, I don't think I quite praised Your name enough.'

'Perhaps you're right,' Himself would agree. 'There may be room for a touch more praise. But I don't want you overdoing it because all this praise, it might go to My knee! And I don't want to become a big-kneed God!'[12]

And so it went on, night after night, week after week, month after month, year after year, decade after decade, century after century, millennium after millennium. Perhaps it wouldn't have been so bad if (i) Raphael had known more than one tune and (ii) if the one tune he did know hadn't been so cretinously turgid.[13]

Each and every night, after we had praised His name, Himself would say, 'Well, it's been another Heavenly day and I'm ready for My bed, so I'm going up the little wooden hill.' And He'd go off to His room. Minutes later He'd come back, saying, 'Where's the staircase?'

And we'd remind Him that we lived in a bungalow.

Then the others would all agree that they'd had a really

12. When He referred to 'knee' He did, of course, mean 'head'. (See end of last chapter. Unless you already have. In which case, don't bother. Instead, why don't you indulge in a spot of wanton carnality?)

13. According to The Author, the tune bore an uncanny resemblance to 'Chirpy Chirpy Cheep Cheep'. Incidentally, this is the thirteenth footnote. It could be very very unlucky for one of you reading it at this moment. Especially if you are reading it on Friday the 13th. And more especially if, as you are reading it, you failed to notice the black cat which crossed your path a moment ago. And even more especially if you ignore the fact that you are just about to walk under a ladder. I have this message for you: Sorry you're not going to finish the book, but I'll tell you the rest of the story when I see you Downstairs!

divine evening and that they were ready to snuggle under the sheets. And Zadkiel would say, 'Yes, an early night for me because I think I'm coming down with a bad moult.' And we'd all go off to our rooms, get down on our knees beside our beds and say our prayers:

'God bless Gabriel, God bless Raphael, God bless Uriel, God Bless Zadkiel, God bless me and God bless Yourself.'

Then they'd all turn in and sleep the sleep of the just, not to say the sleep of the smugly self-righteous. All except me. I would sit up half of the night, staring out in the black, empty, featureless, infinite void of the universe and think, 'There *must* be more to eternal life than this! Somewhere there *has* to be something more interesting.'

But there wasn't.

One evening, after a peculiarly dreadful supper...another of His experiments; this time it was a barbecue. Terribly indigestible, especially the metal legs...Anyway, after it the others were all saying: 'What shall we do tonight?'

'Ummm, that's a tough one.'

'I know! Let's try to persuade Raphael to give us a tune on his harp!'

'Brilliant idea!'

I could stand it no longer. So I said, 'Do you know what I'd *really* like?'

'Yes, Muriel, what you'd *really* like is to join in singing "Let's All Praise His Name!".'

'No, I wouldn't. I'd like to do something else for a change.'

'Something else? Like what?'

'Well, I'd like to go out somewhere and get stoned.'

'You want to go out and get stoned? What a really wizard idea!'

And so we all went out and they stoned me.

The next morning, when I emerged rather later than usual, they asked, 'You're not looking too bright. Didn't you enjoy your night out?'

'Let's just say I've got a terrible headache and my mouth feels as though an ostrich has urinated into it.'

'So you don't like going out and getting stoned.'

'To be quite frank, it wasn't exactly what I had in mind.'

'So, what *did* you have in mind?'

'Well, somehow I thought I might drink something – something other than nectar – and it would make me feel happy and I'd laugh and joke and sing and dance and then stagger to my bed to fall happily into a dreamless sleep. Then I'd wake up in the morning and...'

'And?'

'Have a terrible headache and my mouth would feel like an ostrich had urinated into it.'

'What sort of drink,' they asked, 'would do all that?'

'I don't know, but I think He should invent one.'

'So,' said Gabriel, 'given that you are covered in black and blue bruises which, if I may say so, clash horribly with your tartan wings, and given that you have a terrible headache and that your mouth feels as-though an ostrich – whatever *that* may be – has urinated in it, I suppose that you will never ever want to go out and get stoned again.'

'Not at all. I think I'll do the same thing tonight. After all, having large rocks slung at you is better than listening to Raphael playing the harp.'[14]

So once a week I'd go out with the boys and they'd sling rocks at me. It wasn't much, but it was better than nothing. The others really enjoyed it, especially Gabriel because it gave him good practice for being an avenging angel and built up his pectoral muscles at the same time. And I found that I was starting to enjoy the pain and had quite inadvertently invented masochism billions of years before my good friend Sacher de Masoch gave it his name, and that Gabriel had invented sadism billions of years before Sade gave it her name.[15]

That marked The End of The Middle Bit Before The Real Beginning Actually Began...

---

14. I really hate that instrument and have banned it from Hades. Above the front gate is a sign saying, 'Abandon harp all ye who enter here.'

15. When we pointed out that sadism was named after the Marquis de Sade who specialized in torture and not the pop star Sade, The Author responded: 'Have you heard her sing? She inflicts more pain and punishment than he ever did.'

Chapter...Um??[16]

The Start of The Last Bit Before The Real Beginning Actually Began

 remember waking up one Lawnmower with a particularly bad headache.[17] It was caused, I recall, by an unusually large rock thrown by Gabriel with unnecessary relish. So, in addition to my bruises, I was also uncomfortably sticky from the tomato sauce.[18]

As I lay in my bed I viewed the events of the coming day in Heaven. I would get up as usual. I would say my morning prayers – 'Thank You God for blessing Gabriel. Thank You God for blessing Raphael. Thank You God for blessing Uriel. Thank You God for blessing Zadkiel. Thank You God for blessing me. And most of all, thank You God for blessing Yourself' – as usual. I would have breakfast – ambrosia washed down with nectar – as usual.

After breakfast I would put on my clean white frock as usual. And I would go outside as usual. And within minutes my clean white frock would get grubby as usual. And I would

16. This is Chapter Five. In seeking to confuse, The Author has become confused.

go inside and wash it as usual. Everything would go on as usual. As usual. And as usual, I would be bored rigid. But, unusually, on this particular dark and dismal Lawnmower morning I had an idea.[19]

I leapt from my bed and went rushing into the kitchen where Himself was dishing up breakfast and the others were asking, 'What's for breakfast this morning, God?'

'Well,' He replied, 'I thought that you might like some ambrosia and nectar.'

'Ambrosia and nectar! How absolutely scrummy! You really do spoil us!'

I was bursting with excitement and shouted, 'Listen everyone, I've just had an idea!'

Everyone stopped in their tracks and Himself turned to me and said, 'An idea! You've just had an idea?'

'Yes, I've just had this really great idea!'

And Himself said, 'Well done, Muriel! I never knew you had it in you!'

And the others shouted, 'Yes, well done Muriel! We never knew you had it in you!'

And Himself gazed upon me and said, 'What exactly *is* an "idea"?'

'An "idea"? Well, how can I explain it in words that You'll

---

17. Lawnmower was the fifth day of the week. According to The Author, during the infancy of the universe everything was given an arbitrary name. If the name was kept, if not it was changed and the word given to something else. At that time, the days of the week were Courgette (Sunday), Dishwasher (Monday), Drain (Tuesday), Particle (Wednesday), Lawnmower (Thursday), Gastritis (Friday) and Wubblypoop (Saturday). Of these only Wubblypoop has been lost to linguistics although, according to The Author, it was used in the Atlantan tongue to describe the pus emanating from a large boil after it has been squeezed. As the continent of Atlantis reputedly sank beneath the ocean, there is no way of verifying this claim. Nor another of The Author's assertions that 'Tuesday' was originally the word for using a vacuum cleaner as an enema.

18. Tomato sauce: it seems that Gabriel used to smear rocks with this relish in the mistaken belief that he could eat them.

19. Every morning in Heaven was dark and dismal because Himself had not yet created the sun.

understand? Basically, an "idea" is an image of an external object formed by the mind, isn't it?'

'Of course it is,' He said, 'I knew that. I know everything, being as I am, omnisc..., omnish...omn...oh, what's that word again?'

'Omniscient. It means all-knowing.'

'Exactly, that's Me, omni-what'sname...all-knowing.'

'Excuse me,' said Gabriel, 'but I haven't quite grasped this "idea" thing.'

'Well,' I explained, 'an "idea" is a notion, a thought, an impression. It's any product of intellectual action or of memory and imagination. It's an abstraction, an archetype, a concept, a conjecture, a hypothesis, an inkling, a perception, a surmise, a theory, a vision. That's an "idea".'

And the others were thunderstruck and looked at me aghast until Gabriel said, 'Oh, so *that's* an "idea". Tell me, can you eat it?'

'No, you can't eat it, Gabriel.'

'Pity.'

'At least, I don't think you can.'

'Well, it's not much use to us, is it?'

And God said, 'What is this wonderful, marvellous, terrific, incredible, utterly brilliant "idea"?'

'Well,' I explained, 'it just came to me this morning. I suddenly thought that instead of doing what we usually do all day...'

'Yes?' said Himself.

'We should try doing...'

'Yes?'

'Something...'

'Something. Yes?'

'Well, something...*else*!'

'Something else?'

'Exactly!'

'Something else like what?'

'I don't know like what, my idea hasn't quite got that far. But, basically, I thought we should all do something else for a change.'

'But,' said Himself, 'there isn't anything else. There's only this.'

40

'That's my point. Why can't You, with that infinite omni-potence of which You keep boasting, create something to do?'

'I see,' He said and fell silent.

After a few minutes I said, 'Of course, if You *can't* create something, You only have to say so. I mean, we won't think any the worse of You.'

Then He spake, and when He spake, it was like unto an earthquake that made all Heaven tremble and heave beneath our quivering feet and caused bits of plaster to fall from the ceiling.

'OF COURSE I CAN CREATE SOMETHING!' spake He. 'ANYTHING! I CAN CREATE THINGS THE LIKE OF WHICH YOU CAN'T EVEN IMAGINE. I AM THE LORD THY GOD! I AM THE ALMIGHTY! THE ULTIMATE AND SUPREME PERFECTION WHOSE PUISSANCE IS WITHOUT LIMIT!

THERE IS NOTHING, BUT NOTHING, I CANNOT CREATE!'

And when the trembling and heaving had subsided and after we'd dusted the plaster out of our hair, I said, 'So what's stopping You?'

'I just can't think *what* to create. I mean, it's all very well for you to say, "Go on, create something" but you're not so clever when it comes to suggesting what I might create, are you? So come on, Mr Smartie-Boots, you tell Me what to create. Where are your so-called "ideas" now?'

'We–ell...'

'Yes?'

'Well, just off the top of my head, why don't You try creating somewhere else?'

'What do you mean by "somewhere else"?'

'I mean, somewhere that isn't *here*. Somewhere we could go to for an evening, or could take a trip to on a Courgette afternoon, see the sights and maybe have a picnic.'[20]

---

20. For those of you who can't remember a simple fact from one page to another, 'Courgette' is Sunday. This is the twentieth footnote; it's a little-known fact that twenty is an *incredibly* unlucky number for some. Especially if your name happens to be Peter Chatto and you're reading this in bed while smoking a cigarette. See you soon, Pete!

'And where do you suggest I might put this "somewhere else"?'

'Well, anywhere in the tractless void of infinite space. After all, there's enough of it to choose from.' I pointed at random into the empty vastness and said, 'Why not put it there?'

He followed the direction of my finger, screwed up His eyes, gazed into the meaningless, measureless blankness and said, 'What, there?'

'Yes, that'll do.'

'No, not there. Too...well, meaningless. And also measureless. I have decided, in My infinite wisdom, that it should be a smidgin lower and slightly to the left.'

Typical!

But without more ado He rolled up His sleeves, straightened His halo, climbed on His box and from this exulted position He stared intently into the fathomless depths of space, concentrating all His mental and spiritual energy on one minuscule, measureless and, indeed, meaningless spot. Then, raising His hand, He pointed His finger and boomed:

'I AM THE LORD GOD ALMIGHTY, SUPREME AND OMNIPOTENT BEING, CREATOR OF HEAVEN AND... WELL, JUST HEAVEN SO FAR, BUT THAT'S BESIDE THE POINT...HEAR YE MY WORDS AND OBEY THIS, MY COMMAND:
LET THERE BE...UM..."SOMEWHERE ELSE"!'

No sooner had He uttered these words than, in a deafening crash of thunder, a searing lightning bolt scorched from Him, streaking headlong into the benighted pit of nothingness, speeding ever onwards and outwards until it became but a pinprick of light. And just as it was about to disappear, the void erupted into a holocaust of blazing light, a massive conflagration made even more awesome by its terrible silence.

Eventually, when the blaze diminished and the smoke cleared, we could just make something out, infinitesimal but perceptible and glowing faintly against the surrounding stygian gloom. Something that could only be described as 'something'. And this 'something' was His creation.

We fell involuntarily to our knees, and then abased ourselves, face down, on the ground beneath His feet, quaking before the colossal magnificence of His power.

One by one we raised our fearful faces to gaze upon Him. He stood there, shimmering and golden, as a reverential silence reigned until Gabriel, his voice small and tremulous with wonder, whispered: 'And God said, "Let there be 'somewhere else'." And lo! there *was* "somewhere else"!'

And God Almighty looked down upon us and spake unto us, saying, 'Bloody Norah! It actually *worked*!'

Chapter Something Or Other[21]

The Start of The Last Bit Before The Real Beginning Actually Began...Later That Same Lawnmower...

allelujah! Hallelujah! Hallelujah! God has created "somewhere else"!' shouted Gabriel, Uriel and Zadkiel. 'Hallelujah! Hallelujah! Whatever that means.'

'I've just decided,' said Himself, 'that it means "Praise My Name".'

So Raphael grabbed his harp and started singing:

'Let's all hallelujah!
Let's all hallelujah!
Why don't we all join in and hallelujah?
Yes, hallelujah!
Oh! hallelujah!
There really is nothing better in all of Heaven than hallelujahing!
So let's all hallelujah!'

---

21. This is, of course, Chapter Six. Or is it Chapter Five?

...until God told him to shut up because He had a splitting kneegraine, brought on by exerting His immense powers.[22] Then He turned to me and said, 'There you are, Muriel, you wanted Me to create "somewhere else" and I have. What have you to say to that?'

'Very good. I have to admit I'm impressed. But just one teensy point...'

'Yes?'

'How do we get there?'

'Pardon?'

'What is the point of having "somewhere else" to go, if we can't get there? How are we going to transport ourselves from here to "somewhere else"?'

'Um...er...yes, well, I thought we could perhaps...um ...fly there.'

'Fly there?' said Gabriel.

'Yes, fly there. Using your wings. Remember your wings? They're the large flappy things attached to your back.'

'But,' Gabriel protested, 'You can't seriously mean that we fly all the way to "somewhere else", it must be...oooh, a million, billion, trillion miles away. And we've never flown farther than the wall at the end of the yard.'

And Zadkiel chipped in, 'You don't really expect me to fly a squillion miles when my feathers might moult at any moment! It could be seriously dangerous, not to mention what a fright I'll look when I arrive!'

'Of course,' Raphael added, 'I wouldn't *mind* flying a quintillion miles through the uncharted infinity of space, without a map or even some directions scribbled on the back of an envelope, but I do think someone should stay behind here, just in case the milkman calls.'

'Don't be stupid,' said Himself. 'I haven't created a milkman yet. And even if I had, he wouldn't call until Wubblypoop morning and this is only Later That Same Lawnmower.'

'Well in that case,' said Raphael, 'I'll just stay here and practise my hallelujahs so that I can *really* praise Your name if...I mean, when You return.'

Finally we decided to put it to the vote. Those in favour of

22. A migraine of the knee.

flying – one. Those against – four. Abstentions – me. It was the one and only time I ever abstained from anything in my entire existence, but on this occasion I felt that while I didn't object to stretching my wings and certainly relished an adventure, I wasn't too confident about Himself's skills as a navigator. It's difficult to trust yourself to someone who lives in a one-storey house and still thinks He goes upstairs to bed every night.

'So,' Uriel asked, 'if we're not going to fly, how are we going to get from here to "somewhere else"?'

And He said, 'I don't know! I'm knackered from exerting My immense powers, why doesn't Muriel come up with one of his "ideas". What do you say, Mr Clever Clogs?'

I thought for a moment. 'What we need is a cart, and before You ask, I don't know exactly what a cart is but can't You create something that will carry the six of us in comfort from here to there, and even from hither to yon and back again? And when You've done that, perhaps You'd also like to knock up a couple of horses to draw the cart?'

'Horses?' He said, 'What are horses?'

'I'm not sure, but perhaps they could be large, strong four-legged animals with flowing manes and long swishy tails.'

'Oh, you mean toads. No, I don't want to be whisked from here to "somewhere else" by toads, thank you very much. I am, after all, God, and I do have a certain image to maintain. I like to think that I can create Myself something better than a two toadpower cart.'

So saying, He drew Himself up to His full five feet two inches, pulled in His stomach, puffed out His chest, closed His eyes in concentration and clicked His fingers.

A CLAP! of thunder,
a FLASH! of lightning,
a PUFF! of smoke

and lo! there was a thingy. Not just any thingy but a burning, flame-covered thingy.

And we all said, 'Lo! He's done it again! Yea, this time He's created a burning, flame-covered thingy! Tell us, O Lord, what is it that You have created just by clicking Your fingers?'

'That is a chariot. Which is like a cart but posher, having, as it does, three extra letters in its name, not to mention independent suspension on both wheels. Is it not finger-clicking good? And no, Gabriel, you can't eat it.'

'Pity,' said Gabriel hungrily as the flames roared higher around it, 'because it's done to a turn.'

'As you can see,' continued Himself, 'this is not just any old chariot, but My extra-special Chariot of Fire, complete with optional extras like rear parking light and built-in cigar lighter. But without old-fashioned toadpower. Now hop aboard and we'll take a look at "somewhere else".'

Thus did we voyage through the immense black bleakness of space aboard His Chariot of Fire, whose flames illumined the dreadful darkness, casting light all around and causing us to sweat like pigs. In the twinkling of a...well, a twinkle ...it had transported us across the measureless miles and landed us on "somewhere else".

As we surveyed His creation, Himself said, 'So, Muriel, what do you think of "somewhere else"? Is it not good?'

And I gazed upon it, upon the shack painted ditchwater brown and sludge green, upon the plumbing which left a lot to be desired, like pipes, running water and a toilet seat and replied, 'Unless my eyes deceive, it is exactly the same as Heaven.'

'So?'

'So, call me naive if you will, but somehow I thought it would be different.'

'No, I will not call you Naive as you already have a perfectly good name. And what do you mean by different? When you asked Me to create "somewhere else" you didn't mention anything about it being different.'

'Swipe me,' I thought to myself, 'The Supreme Being has the I.Q. of a radish.'

And He said, 'I read that thought, Muriel! And I take it as a compliment, seeing as I will one day create an intelligence that is almost equal to Mine and which will run the universe while I am taking a well-earned rest. That superbrain will be called a "radish". Now, what's all this "different" business?'[23]

'How shall I put this?' I said, 'Look, it never occurred to me that The Supreme Being, whose intelligence is infinite and even greater than a radish's will be, would make "somewhere else" exactly the same as the place we were getting away from. So exactly and precisely the same that "somewhere else" doesn't have a toilet seat either.'

'Really,' He said, 'I go to all the bother and effort of creating a whole new place in the infinite universe, not to mention providing first-class, fire-driven transport and remembering to pack a hamper of nectar and ambrosia in case we feel peckish and still he complains! Some archangels are never satisfied!'

'Well,' said Gabriel, 'I really like it.'

'So do I,' agreed Raphael.

'Me too,' said Uriel.

'I think it's absolutely gorgeous,' said Zadkiel, 'it reminds me of home.'

'So there, Mr Spoilsport!', said Himself.

Patiently I explained that the whole purpose of creating somewhere else was to have a place we could visit that wasn't anything like Heaven, somewhere completely and utterly different.

So God said, 'All right! All right! I'll make it different. Anything to stop you complaining.' And He clicked his fingers.

A CLAP! of thunder

A FLASH! of lightning

And a PUFF! of smoke

23. Eventually, He did create the radish and it did have an intelligence vastly superior to that of any other life-form in the universe, except His. But the radish was so mind-bogglingly intelligent that when it thought about how intelligent it was, its mind literally boggled at the sheer effort. Having reduced itself to an I.Q. of zero, it settled contentedly for being a salad vegetable which gets its revenge for being eaten by causing acute indigestion and making people belch embarrassingly at exactly the wrong moment.

'And lo!,' He said, 'it has come to pass! The "somewhere else" is different!'

And the others all jumped up and down and chanted, 'Lo! He's done it yet again! What a blinder! It is completely different! Yea, verily, now we have a shack painted dingy grey and muddy beige.'

And He spake, saying, 'Nay, verily, it is not dingy grey and muddy beige, it is Candyfloss Pink and Mediterranean Blue.'

To which the others replied, 'Oh, sorry, our mistake!'

But I said, 'If You think those colours are Candyfloss Pink and Mediterranean Blue, You need Your eyes tested!'

'There is nothing wrong with My eyes.'

'Is that so? Then why, despite Your infinite wisdom – about which we hear so much – do You seem to have difficulty distinguishing one shade from another?'

'I do not have difficulty,' He snapped, 'I am infallible. And omnipotent. And that other word meaning "all-knowing" which seems to have slipped My mind for the moment. You're just saying that because you're envious of My immense powers. You, Muriel, are purple with envy.'

'You mean green with envy.'

'DON'T ARGUE!'

'I'm not arguing, I'm simply pointing out an error of fact. There's no need to get so ratty just because You won't admit You're colour-blind.'

'I AM NOT COLOUR-BLIND!'

'Excuse me, but You are.'

'IF YOU ARGUE WITH ME ONCE MORE, I'LL TURN YOU INTO A TOAD!'

'Well, please Yourself but it doesn't seem a very adult way of ending a discussion.'

'RIGHT! THAT'S IT! YOU'VE ASKED FOR IT! JUST ONE CLICK OF MY FINGERS AND...'

And nothing.

'Are You,' I asked, 'having trouble getting Your immense powers to work?'

'NO, I'M NOT. IF YOU MUST KNOW, I'M JUST HAVING TROUBLE CLICKING MY FINGERS.'

'In that case,' said Gabriel, ever-helpful, 'lick Your thumb and forefinger. That's right. Now try again.'

49

'AS I WAS SAYING, IT TAKES JUST ONE CLICK OF MY FINGERS AND...

CLAP!
FLASH!
PUFF!

'So there! And what have you got to say to that, Mr Toad?'
'Um...Neeeeeeeeigh!'

Chapter Seven
or Maybe Eight[24]

The Start of The Last Bit Before The Etc., Etc.

A Teensy Bit Later That Same Lawnmower...

All things considered, being a toad wasn't so bad. Obviously, suddenly having four legs took some getting used to, especially deciding which should be on the ground and which should be off the ground at any one time. After rather a lot of falling over I finally got the hang of having a leg at each corner which is rather like being an occasional table. In my time, of course, I have been an occasional table. I've also been an occasional wardrobe and, when it has suited my evil purpose a very, very occasional three-piece suite in uncut moquette. (When you do as much seducing as I, it comes in handy being able to change your form at will. Saves you a lot of unpleasantness from cuckolded husbands. Or, indeed, wives, depending upon the gender of the lucky person I happen to be seducing. However, you have to be quick-witted. I recall one occasion when an outraged husband burst in just as I had enjoyed carnal knowledge of his spouse. In a flash I changed form. But I think he was

24. This is definitely, indubitably and unarguably Chapter Seven. We think.

suspicious about finding his wife in bed with a potting shed. Not that he could do much about it. His lawyer advised him he was unlikely to get a divorce on the grounds of her adultery with a semi-permanent garden structure, even given that they lived on the twenty-seventh floor of a highrise block of flats. And further advised him to seek psychiatric help. But not until he'd presented a hefty bill for his services.)

There I go, digressing again. Where was I? Ah, yes, being a toad. Not a bad life. I liked having the flowing mane and really loved the swishy tail. In fact, I loved it so much that I later adopted a tail of my own which, despite what you hear, I don't wear all the time but keep for special occasions. You should see me on Gala Orgy Nights in Hades, dressed up to the nines in my top hat, white tie and tail.[25]

As you've almost certainly guessed, unless you're particularly dense, which, after my experience of tricking and deceiving countless generations of you gullible fools, wouldn't surprise me, The Great Fraud got it wrong again. What He thought was a toad was, of course, a horse and, as a horse, I was quite content. Not to say, really very happy.

You see, horses have certain things that archangels don't. Apart from the two extra legs, the flowing mane and the swishy tail, I very soon became aware that I now possessed something else. And a very large something else at that. How shall I put this? Well, you never hear it said of any man that he's hung like a toad, do you? And you certainly don't hear it of archangels who, despite certain attributes like halos and enormous wings, are notably deficient in the groin area.

25. Every night is Orgy Night in Hades but once in a while we have a Gala Orgy at which the guests must perform seven different sexual acts with an animal, vegetable or mineral with which they've never previously had an intimate relationship. Sometimes they have to perform one sexual act with seven different animals, vegetables or minerals; I leave the details to the creature who arranges the evening, Bogsnatch. I call him my orgyniser. Not a very good joke but it amuses him. Mind you, most things amuse him, including wrenching the wings off rabbits. You didn't know rabbits had wings did you? And of course they don't, until Bogsnatch has hammered them into their backs with six-inch nails. A rather simple-minded hobby but it keeps him entertained.

To put it bluntly, they have nothing whatsoever there. Gabriel, for example, had even less between his legs than he had between his ears, which is saying something considering he was not quite as intelligent as your average radish, even after its mind had so spectacularly boggled.

You may, therefore, be able to imagine my surprise when it became apparent to me that I was now the possessor of an added attribute. And you may possibly be able to imagine my delight when I discovered that this attribute could do something considerably more interesting and enjoyable than just making water.[26]

I hadn't been a horse more than a few minutes when I started to experience what can best be described as 'stirrings'. (Actually, they can best be described as something quite different, but the publishers, miserable maggots that they are, censored my manuscript. May they rot in Hull.)[27]

These delicious 'stirrings' were as nothing I'd ever experienced before. Mind you, I'd hardly experienced *anything* before in the way of sensual delights, least of all of the gastronomic variety. My only physical pleasure had come from a comfy but chaste bed and being on the receiving end of large and jagged rocks. I realize the latter is not to everyone's taste, but then most of you don't know what you're missing – if you did you wouldn't be quite so squeamish about such delectably diverting activities as sucking the living brains out of nuns. But that's neither here nor there. It's somewhere else entirely, usually a convent in the dead of night.

26. *Publisher's note:* this raises an interesting theological and, indeed, biological question: if archangels do not possess the organ in question, how do they go to the toilet? The Author's answer is, 'They don't, archangels have no bodily functions at all.' In which case, we asked, why does he claim to have been so critical of the alleged toilet facilities offered in Heaven? To which he replied, 'I lied.'

27. *Miserable Maggots' note:* for any readers who are not conversant with the geography of The British Isles, Hull is a city on the east coast of England, standing on the estuary of the River Humber. It was once the centre of a thriving fishing industry but is now more noted as a major container port. We would like to make it clear that in our opinion this bustling little metropolis bears absolutely no relation to Hell, except, of course, that it too is a God-forsaken place.

All-in-all, I rated these unexpected 'stirrings' as being vastly superior to both a comfy bed and a jagged rock. However, in my utter innocence, I was puzzled. I didn't understand the purpose of said 'stirrings'. I was becoming increasingly aware of a growing presence in my loin but perplexed as to what to do about it. And, indeed, with it.

At first I thought it might be some form of extra limb, a fifth leg perhaps, but rejected the notion when I realized that long though it was, it didn't quite reach the ground. Next I wondered if it served a similar purpose to my swishy tail as a device for deterring flies and pests. I swished it vigorously once or twice, so vigorously that it smacked sharply against my offside back leg, causing considerable pain and rather less pleasure than I'd hoped. I realized it would have been useless as a fly-whisk unless one managed an incredible, almost impossible, degree of accuracy.

Once I'd regained my breath and my eyes had stopped smarting, I noticed that this experiment resulted in my 'stirrings' becoming diminished. Indeed, they had almost disappeared, which was extremely disappointing because I was just beginning to thoroughly enjoy them.

But, try as I might, I could not regain them and in their absence I decided to put all four of my legs to the test with a short canter. Having managed to reach a respectable speed after only tripping twice when my nearside back became entangled with my offside front, and having practised a bit of whinnying and nostril-flaring, I looked around for further entertainment, preferably of the 'stirrings' variety. Finding none, I settled for a session of mane-tossing and tried pricking up my ears.

No sooner had I pricked up my ears (which should not, in any way, be construed as discovering a use for my 'stirrings') than I heard a sound, a sound like muffled thunder, as though Himself was speaking to me from a very great distance.

Looking around I discovered the source of the noise – thudding hooves. I was not alone. Rushing towards me was another four-legged creature, complete with flowing mane and swishing tail. It approached at a gallop, without once mistaking its back legs for its front, slowed to a trot and then reared on its hind legs.[28]

It opened its mouth and said, 'Cesspit!'

'Pardon?' said I.

'Cesspit, that's my name.'

'Cesspit', I said. 'What a lovely name!'

'Thank you,' it said. 'What's yours?'

'Um...well, actually, it's Muriel. But I'm thinking of changing it.'

'Yes,' said Cesspit, 'you should. Around here "Muriel" means "vile tapeworm that gnaws into the gut, has lamentable table manners and never ever says 'Pardon' after it breaks wind".'

'What do you suggest I change it to?'

'Well, "Pustule" is very popular at the moment, but looking at you I would suggest "Dobbin" which means "beautifully formed but having a coat that is a rather curious sort of tartan, comprising vibrant green and a shade of orange that some might describe as 'electric' but which I consider to be on the vulgar side of garish".'

'Yes,' I said, 'horrible isn't it?'

'Oh, I don't know. On you it looks good. You've got the fetlocks to carry it off.'

'Do you really think so?'

'Certainly.'

'Thank you.'

'You're welcome. Now, do you want to screw yourself brainless or what?'

'I beg your pardon?'

'I said, "Do you want to..."'

'Yes, I know what you said, but what does it mean?'

'What does it mean? Where have you been?'

28. When asked how it was possible for another creature to exist before God has created it, The Author replied, 'I was in the space–time continuum where anything and everything is possible. It's a strange and mysterious plane of being where the impossible happens so regularly that it becomes commonplace and miraculous phenomena are hardly worth mentioning. The space–time continuum is so impossibly amazing that even the trains arrive according to schedule, you can find a policeman when you need one and the taxi drivers actually know where they are going. Although, of course, they're still surly and rude. Even where the impossible is possible, some things, like polite and caring cab drivers, are just *too* impossible.'

'Well, actually, I've been in Heaven.'

'In Heaven! Pull the other one. No, don't bother, I'll pull your other one.'

Which is exactly what Cesspit did and immediately I began to feel my 'stirrings' again.

'Well, at least you know what *that* is for.'

'Er...well...actually I don't.'

And so Cesspit told me. Told me about males, which, apparently is what I was, and females, which is what she was. And she told me precisely and in graphic anatomical detail what males do to females when they both have 'stirrings'. As she told me all this I became greatly 'stirred'. Seeing how tremendously and obviously 'stirred' I was she said, 'So, do you want to screw yourself brainless?'

'Yes, please, if that's all right with you.'

She sighed resignedly, 'Oh all right, you've talked me into it, you silver-tongued smoothie.'

Then she winked, licked her lips and, flicking her tail in the most delightfully lascivious manner, turned around to display her pert, round perfectly-formed hocks, saying, 'Come and get it, big boy!'

I needed no second bidding. With one bound I was behind her, ears pricked, nostrils flaring. I threw back my head, tossed my mane, reared up on to my back legs, and with a cry of joy, thrust my newly-found tumescence towards her and...

CLAP!
FLASH!
PUFF!

Chapter...Um...The One After Last[29]

Enormous Breasts

CLAP!

  FLASH!

    PUFF!

ne second I was about to savour my first taste of erotic delight, the next I found myself back at the dingy shack, peering into the gloom, standing in front of Himself and the others, lounging on the ground.

'Welcome back, Muriel! Being a merciful God, I have decided to forgive you and so I've returned you to the infinite joys of Heaven. I trust your short but miserable existence as a toad has taught you the error of your ways and that in future we'll have no more of your nonsense. Now, sit down, have an ambrosia sandwich and we'll say no more about it.'

'Yes,' carolled the others, 'have an ambrosia sandwich, which He has cleverly invented by putting ambrosia between two bits of sliced manure! Verily, this sandwich is the most blissful of all the myriad and wondrous things in God's creation!'

'You wouldn't say that if you'd ever experienced a "stirring".'

'Pardon?'

---

29. We are almost certain this is Chapter Eight. But who cares?

'Nothing. Now, if you don't mind, I'll forgo the sandwich, I just want to pop inside to check something.'

I went indoors to my bedroom. I locked the door behind me, closed the curtains and, hidden from prying eyes, I lifted up my frock, pulled down my scanty French directoire knickers and looked between my legs to find...nothing.

I was once again what I had always been, a genderless archangel. An archangel robbed of the source of the most exquisite pleasure I had ever experienced. And, worse still, robbed of my ultimate sensual experience.

I wept bitter tears of frustration.

It was so unfair! All I had needed were another couple of minutes. Just two more minutes of lunging towards those pert little hocks and my pleasure would have been consummated. I had been trembling on the very brink of physical ecstasy, hovering tantalizingly close to the eruption of bodily desire and in an instant my joy had been snatched from me. At that very instant He had plucked me from the erotic brink; with one click of His fingers He had cheated me of my pleasure.

He had timed it to perfection. An instant later and bliss would have been mine. And I knew that the old bastard knew. He knew exactly what He was doing, exactly what He was denying me. Even then, as I wept in frustrated rage, He was sitting outside, munching His sandwich and laughing hysterically to Himself.

I would never forgive Him. I vowed there and then to get my revenge, I didn't care how long I waited, I would have my retribution, even if it took me a hundred thousand million years.

In fact it took me 99,999,999,999 years, seven months and six days. And the reason it took so long was The Really Triff And Absolutely Brill Plan...

Meanwhile, Back in The Space–Time Continuum . . .

. . . a horse called Cesspit is saying, 'Come and get it, big boy!'

CLAP!

FLASH!

PUFF!

'Pardon? Where's he gone? Buggered off without so much as a goodbye! Typical! Bloody men, get you all worked up and then...nothing! Who needs them? Anyway, I didn't really fancy him, especially not in that ridiculous tartan coat. He's no great loss, for all his fine talk about his "stirrings", that stallion was hung just like a man, poor sod'.

At which point she was struck in the rear by a hurtling express train that was precisely 1.8 seconds behind schedule.

As a result of the impact the train was completely wrecked and Cesspit experienced an orgasm so gut-churningly intense that her brain imploded and she spent the rest of her life believing she was a toad. The rest of her life was, sadly, brief. She drowned when trying to hop from the edge of a pond on to a water-lily which was ill-equipped to take the weight of a lust-crazed horse.

At exactly the same instant, three and three-quarter miles away, a taxi driver was just abusing a passenger for the meanness of his tip when he had a mystic revelation. A vision came to him and revealed one of the great mysteries of the universe – he discovered where flies go in winter. As a result he drove his cab there, taking the long route via the airport and light industrial estate. After three frustrating weeks lost in a contra-flow gyratory system, he gave up in disgust and turned down a dirty alley.

Why a large bearded woman should linger around a contra-flow gyratory system, waiting to approach taxi drivers and hiss out of the side of her mouth, 'Pssst! Wanna buy a dirty alley', is an unfathomable enigma.

But anything is possible in the space–time continuum.[30]

---

30. The more observant among you may have noticed that, despite the title of this chapter, there has not been one single reference to enormous breasts. I was going to call the chapter 'The Start of The End Bit Before The Real Beginning Actually Began... A Teensy-Weensy Bit Later That Same Lawnmower...' But somehow 'Enormous Breasts' seemed more eye-catching.

Chapter Nine[31]

The Really Triff And Absolutely Brill Plan

ursing my grudge in my heart, I determined not to give any sign of grievance. I readjusted my clothing over my non-existent groin, wiped the salt tears from my eyes and returned outside.

'Hello, Muriel,' said Gabriel, 'did you find what you were looking for?'

'No.'

'I'll bet it's behind the "sofa".'

'I doubt it.'

'Let me go and have a look,' cried Uriel, 'I *love* looking under the "sofa"!'

'Don't bother. Actually, I'm quite peckish, are there any of those ambrosia sandwiches left?'

'No, we've eaten them all.'

'Well, thank you, thanks so very much.'

'No thanks needed, it was our pleasure!'

Himself, who'd been taking a nap in the afternoon gloom, abruptly woke up and declared, 'I've been thinking!'

---

31. Amazingly, this really *is* Chapter Nine. Honest.

'Hallelujah! God's been thinking! Tell us, O Lord, what have You been thinking?'

'One of the things I've been thinking is how incredible it is being Me! I can think even when I'm taking a nap! Is there no end to My genius?'

The others agreed that there wasn't.

'Just as I suspected. Anyway, apart from thinking how amazing it is that I'm thinking while taking a nap, I've also been thinking that I really quite enjoy this creating things lark, even though it is tiring and liable to give Me a headache, and I'd like to do more of it. So I've worked out this Really Triff And Absolutely Brill Plan.'

The others all clapped their hands and chortled, 'Oh, goody, goody! A Really Triff And Absolutely Brill Plan is just what we were hoping You'd work out! So, don't keep us in suspense any longer, what *is* this Really Triff And Etc., Etc?'

'Well, I'm so pleased with the way that "somewhere else" has turned out that I have decided, in My infinite wisdom, about which I may have spoken once or twice before, that I'm going to create more "somewhere elses". What do you think of that?'

'We think that truly this is Really The Triff-est And Absolutely Brill-est Plan of the type that only You, in Your infinite wisdom of which You may have spoken once or twice and maybe even thrice before, could come up with!'

He proceeded to detail The Plan.

'I have decided that there will be lots and lots of "somewhere elses", scattered throughout the firmament. And each will be a different "somewhere else" from the other. Some, for example, will be like as unto huge lumps of rock of the sort that you fling at Muriel but much, much bigger. Others will be enormous balls of seething gases. Some will be tiny and dainty, giving off pretty little glows of light that will twinkle and sparkle in the firmament and yet others will be truly massive and colossal and composed entirely of green cheese.'

The others all clapped their hands, jumped up and down and trilled, 'By golly, He's done it yet again! Blimey O'Reilly, He really is the sort of God you can look up to, even if He is definitely on the short side for a Supreme Being!'

And Gabriel added, 'This green cheese stuff, can you eat it?'

And God said, 'I don't know because I haven't created it yet. But even if you can, I don't want you gobbling up My beautiful "somewhere elses" as soon as I have created them.'

And He turned to me and said, 'Well, Muriel, what do you think of My Really Triff And Absolutely Brill Plan?'

'It sounds like a lot of hard work to me.'

'It will be hard work, Muriel, because all of you will help Me in this great endeavour. I will do all the creative work, like thinking up the ideas and sketching the designs for the "somewhere elses" and you will do all the heavy manual labour like shifting them around the firmament. And all this arduous toil will keep you so busy that you, Mr Misery Guts, won't have time to moan and whine and bitch and generally stir up trouble.

'My Really Brill And Absolutely Triff Plan will occupy us all, and especially *you*, for the next 99,999,999,999 years, seven months and six days, give or take a day. Yea, verily it can be said that God makes work for idle hands!'

And I contemplated the 99,999,999,999 years, seven months and six-ish joyless days of menial labour that lay ahead, days without 'stirrings', and said, 'I don't suppose You'd consider turning me back into a toad?'

'No!'

Chapter Ten

The Next 99,999,999,999 Years, Six Months And Twenty-Nine Days...

The next 99,999,999,999 years, six months and twenty-nine days seemed like an eternity. And, of course, they would be an eternity to the likes of you because you have a brief life-span which I, with my many guiles and subterfuges, attempt to make all the briefer in order to speed you to the bosom, not to mention the groin, of my family in Hades. But when you are infinite, millennia usually pass in the blinking of an eye.[32]

These millennia did not. The time dragged. For each of those 36,500,000,000,819 days we worked from dawn to dusk.

---

32. I'd just like to say how much I appreciate the help that many of you – particularly smokers, drinkers and drug addicts – give me in this task. It makes my job so much easier. And before those of you who have given up these delicious but deadly habits get too smug, allow me to remind you that the road to Hell is paved with good intentions. In fact, you might as well surrender to your vices because I'm going to get you one way or the other.
Publishers' note: The road to Hell should not be confused with the road to Hull, the A1, which, due to local government cutbacks, isn't paved at all.

No, that's not quite accurate; for 36,500,000,000,818 of them we worked from dawn to dusk. But on the first of them we worked from dusk to dusk as Himself had not yet created the seething mass of gases that was our sun.

On that very first morning we awoke to discover Himself was already up. In fact, He was about seven feet up, hovering cross-legged above the kitchen table, His eyes tightly closed, chanting to Himself, 'I am the champion! I am the champion! I am the champion!' Eventually He became aware of our presence and, blushing slightly, He explained, 'I'm just getting Myself psyched-up for the enormous task that lies before Me.'

'I didn't realize,' I said, 'that making breakfast was so taxing of Your omnipotence.'

'I shall ignore that facetious remark, except to say that in future I shall not be making breakfast. It is, I feel, a task too humble for The Supreme Being who has better things to do with His time like creating galaxies, solar systems, planets, stars and other celestial sundries. From now on you will each take turns to make the meals while I devote My energy to conceiving the multitudinous miracles that constitute My Really Triff And Absolutely Brill Plan.

'So, for the next thirty-six thousand, five hundred million eight hundred and eighteen days you Gabriel and you Raphael and Uriel and Zadkiel will be on brekky duty.'

'Yes, Lord,' they said obediently. 'But what about Muriel? What will he do for the next thirty-six thousand, five hundred million, eight hundred and eighteen days?'

'I have a very special and important task for Muriel, a task that, in My Infinite Wisdom, which I may have mentioned now and again, I have devised especially for him. Every day for the next thirty-six thousand, five hundred million, eight hundred and eighteen days Muriel will do the washing up. Perhaps that will teach him not to make Smart Alec remarks.'

And so it came to pass that for the next thirty-six thousand, five hundred million, eight hundred and eighteen days I did the washing up every morning. But what no one realized in all that time is that I washed their plates, cups, knives, forks and spoons by spitting on them and wiping them with a pair of my old knickers. Not a particularly evil deed compared

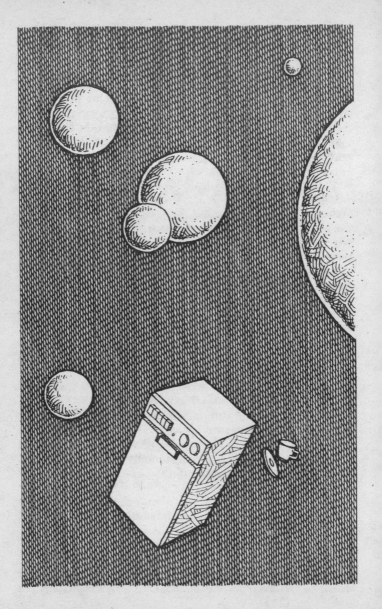

with the depths of depraved wickedness I was to plumb later, but at the time it was the naughtiest thing any archangel had ever done.

After breakfast and having finished the washing up on that very first morning, Himself gathered us around Him and spake, saying, 'This is the first morning of My Really Triff And Absolutely Brill Plan and I intend to start as I will continue, by creating something. Something that will amaze and astound you. And, as this is the start of our great enterprise together, I will allow you to choose what I will create. Any suggestions?'

'Well,' I said, 'what about creating an automatic dish-washer?'

'Shut up, Muriel, unless you want to be scrubbing the kitchen floor every evening for the next thirty-six thousand, five hundred million, eight hundred and eighteen days. Now, let's have some sensible suggestions. Gabriel?'

And Gabriel thought hard for several moments and said, 'Well, Lord, You remember how You created "somewhere else"?'

'Indeed I do.'

'How about creating another "somewhere else"?'

'Yes, that's a really topping idea,' the others chimed. 'Why not create another "somewhere else" and make it exactly like the "somewhere else" You've already created?'

'I was hoping,' said Himself, 'for something a trifle more challenging. I do so hate to repeat Myself.'

'In that case,' said Gabriel, 'maybe this new "somewhere else" could be much, much bigger.'

'Or much, much smaller,' said Raphael.

'Or maybe a bit squarer,' said Uriel.

'Or,' said Zadkiel, 'perhaps it could be slightly...um...furrier.'

'Furrier?'

'Yes. Furrier. Or even...er...wobblier. And when I say "wobblier", perhaps I mean it could be a bit more squiggly in a droopy sort of way. Or something.'

'Thank you, Zadkiel, for those invaluable suggestions. I must remember to make a careful note of them and throw it away. In the meantime, I shall ignore all your suggestions and create something of My own. And what I'm going to create are...mountains.'

'Ooh, goody goody gumdrops! God is going to create mountains! Whatever they may be.'

'Whatever they are, Lord,' said Gabriel, 'could You make them edible?'

But Himself was not listening, He had screwed up His eyes in intense concentration, raised His hand and, after a sharp intake of breath, He intoned:

'LET THERE BE MOUNTAINS!'

And He clicked His fingers...

CLAP!
FLASH!
PUFF!

When the smoke had cleared and our eyes had recovered from the dazzling light, we blinked in amazement at the sight which presented itself.

'By jingo!' we all shouted, 'He's only gone and done it again! Blow me, no sooner did The Lord say, "Let there be mountains", than there *were* mountains!'

'Verily,' quoth Gabriel, 'look at the unimaginable height of them!'

'Yea,' quoth Raphael, 'look at the awesome width of them!'

'Yea and verily!' quoth Uriel, 'look at the fearsome graniteness of them!'

'Yea, verily and lo!' quoth Zadkiel, 'look at the pretty water gushing out of the top of them!'

'Pardon?,' quoth Himself.

And Gabriel quoth back, 'Well, I quothed: "Verily, look at the unimaginable height of them!" Then Raphael quothed, "Yea! Look at the awesome..." '

'Forget all that. What was it that Zadkiel was just quothing?'

'All I quothed was, "Look at the pretty water gushing out of the top of them".'

And Himself looked and saw. 'I said "Let there be mountains." NOT fountains! What's the point of being omnipotent if I can't give the simplest order without something going wrong?'

And the others tried to placate Him, saying, 'Mountains, fountains, what's the difference?'

'The difference, dummies, is that I can't have a huge range of fountains spewing billions of gallons of water all over the place. Think of the mess it will make of My nice clean brand-new planets. It'll make them soggy. And there's nothing, but nothing, worse than a soggy planet.'

That's all He knew. But, of course, He'd never been rudely interrupted in the middle of a rattling good 'stirring'. I didn't actually point that out to Him. Instead, I asked, 'So, what are You going to do about these five-mile high fountains, which even now are pouring water at an alarming rate all over Heaven?'

'Um…well…I suppose I'll just have to uncreate them.'

'And how will You do that?'

'By reversing the whole process. Now stand back and give Me room to think.'

He unscrewed His eyes, lowered His hand and, after a sharp exhalation of breath, He outtoned:

'!SNIATNUOM EB EREHT TEL'

And He unclicked His fingers…

!FFUP

!HSALF

!PALC

And we witnessed it and cried: 'Crikey! He's only gone and undone it! Well, I'll be hornswoggled! No sooner did The Lord say, "!sniatnuom eb ereht teL", than there *were* no fountains!'

And Himself said, 'You ain't seen nothin' yet.' And He raised His hand yet again and screwed up His eyes and commanded:

'LET THERE BE MOUNTAINS!

That's mountains with an "m"! As in "m" for...um...'

'As in "m" for manure?', I suggested, helpfully.

'No! As in "m" for mnemonic!'

And with that the old show-off clicked His fingers...

CLAP!

FLASH!

PUFF!

And we witnessed it and cried, 'Stone the crows! He's done it one more time! No sooner did The Lord say, "Let there be mountains with an 'm', as in 'm' for mnemonic," than there *were* mountains!'

Himself did not yet unscrew His eyes. Instead, He said, 'You're quite sure they are mountains, with an "m" for mnemonic, and not fountains with an "f" for...well, for fotograph?'

'No,' we assured Him, 'they are definitely *not* fountains because there is no pretty water gushing out of the top of them.'

'Well, thank Me for that,' He said.

'Excuse me for saying this,' said I. 'Not that I know anything about mountains, but somehow I expected them to be bigger.'

'Bigger?' He said, slowly opening His eyes.

'Yes. Bigger; taller, wider and more sort of, well, mountainous.'

He looked at them, all five inches of them, and said, 'Yes, I suppose they could be somewhat bigger.'

'And pardon me if I'm wrong,' I continued, 'but I also had the impression that they might be rockier.'

'Rockier?'

'Yes. Somehow I thought they'd be made of rock and granite and maybe marble instead of, well, crumbly bits of earth.'

He looked at them again and said, 'Yes, I suppose *some* people might expect them to be a touch rockier. But what you don't understand, Muriel, is that I have wrought a miracle. I, in My omnipotence, have done what no other being could do, I have made molehills out of mountains. Is not My power awesome and wondrous in the extreme?'

And the others all hymned, 'Yea, verily, Your power *is* awesome and wondrous in the extreme. And we really, truly like Your mountains, even though they tend towards the small and crumbly.'

'All right, all right,' He said, 'You don't have to go on about their smallness and crumbliness. To prove that I am truly and unquestionably omnipotent, I will now turn these admittedly not very large or particularly craggy mountains into something that will take your breath away.'

So saying, He went through His familiar little ritual yet again intoning:

'LET THERE BE MOUNTAINS. AND LET THEM BE
HUGE, MASSIVE AND BLOODY GI-NORMOUS!'

CLAP!

FLASH!

PUFF!

'Cor! Is there no end to His true and unquestionable omnipotence? No sooner had The Lord said, "Let there be mountains. And let them be huge, massive and bloody gi-normous!", than there were huge, massive and bloody gi-normous mountains!'

'It's nothing,' He murmured modestly. 'Any Supreme Being could do it.'

And we chanted, 'Not only have You made huge, massive and bloody gi-normous mountains appear but, even more incredibly, You have also made our shack completely disappear!'

'What? Have I? I mean, of course I have! It is exactly as I intended! Um, just remind Me, where did I make the shack disappear to?'

'Difficult to tell, but it seems to be under the huge, massive and bloody gi-normous mountains. As if You didn't know.'

'Of course, I knew. Well, I can't stand here all day chit-chatting to you, I've got galaxies to create. So you lot will have to get our shack back.'

'How do we do that, O Lord?'

'It's obvious. Move the mountains!'

'Move the mountains? How? What will move mountains?'

'Faith! Faith will move mountains.'

'But we don't know anyone called Faith.'

'In that case you'll just have to do it yourselves, won't you? Now get on with it, I want those mountains out of here before bedtime!'

Chapter Eleven

The Next 99,999,999,999 Years, Six Months And Twenty-Nine Days... Continued...

S o we moved the mountains, exactly 167 yards to the left. And we found the remains of the shack and re-erected it. And at the end of the day, while we were taking a well-earned rest, Himself inspected our work and said, 'Not bad. But I wanted those mountains moved exactly *159* yards to the *right*. Can't I trust you to do the simplest little chore?'

And I said, 'We've been having a chat among ourselves and we've decided that if we're going to spend the next thirty-six thousand, five hundred million, eight hundred and eighteen days lugging huge, massive and bloody gi-normous mountains from one place to another, we need and deserve better working conditions. So we've compiled a list of demands.'

'Demands?'

'Yes, my fellow archangels and I have conferred and we demand an agreement about our terms of employment – the length of the working week, remuneration and, of course, the length and frequency of nectar breaks.

'But even more important than those, I am mandated by my colleagues to bring to Your attention the potentially dangerous situation arising from the low level of ambient lighting. The lack of adequate lighting is appalling. How can my fellow workers and I be expected to move entire mountain ranges in this perpetual gloom? Three times today Comrade Uriel nearly dropped an alp by tripping over one of those pointy things at the top of another mountain. And Comrade Zadkiel nearly had a very nasty accident – almost resulting in a serious wing loss situation – when he slid down that horrible cold white slippery stuff that covers the pointy things. And all because we couldn't see where we were going.

'Frankly, the light from a halo is just not sufficient for the job. If You don't supply some efficient lighting we're refusing to carry on with the work.'

'Refusing!'

'You heard me. We've discussed it and we're all agreed. No light, no work. It's unanimous.'

He looked about Him and his gaze fell on Gabriel.

'You agree with this?'

'Um. Well, "agree" is putting it rather strongly, Let's say that...er...it seems reasonable to me. But, of course, if You've got other ideas...'

Then He turned to Raphael and boomed, 'Are you part of this conspiracy?'

'Lord, I can answer that in two ways.'

'Go ahead.'

'The first way is to say, "No".'

'And the second way?'

'Is to say, "Absolutely, positively and unequivocally no".'

'I'll take that as a negative, then. And what about you, Uriel, and you, Zadkiel?'

And Uriel and Zadkiel looked at Him and opened their mouths and spake, saying, 'Mibbly bomble murgly eeerghft.'

'I see. Well, let's assume that it is not a vote of support for Muriel's demands.'

He looked again upon me. 'So much for unanimity Muriel. In view of your comrades' lack of enthusiasm, do you retract your demand?'

'No.'

'I see. This is a very serious situation. You have had the audacity to challenge My authority. The authority of The Lord God Almighty, The Supreme And Omnipotent Being! And for it you shall be punished, punished more severely than any being has ever been punished.'

'You're going to turn me back into a toad?'

'Certainly not! This punishment is far, far more severe. This is My judgement on you, Muriel, for your heinous and grievous sin. Henceforth, until the end of time, you shall scrub the kitchen floor.'

The others all gasped. 'You mean, he's got to scrub the kitchen floor as well as do the washing up?'

'That is My command. But that is not the end of it. Because of the grave and unique nature of your crime, I ordain that this very night you, Muriel, will go straight to bed. Without any supper!'

The others fell to wailing, 'No supper! Muriel can't have any ambrosia or nectar! Verily that is a severe and bitter punishment! Not that we're saying he doesn't deserve it, You understand, but we never expected anything as harsh as this. Take pity on Muriel, O Lord! Reconsider Your decision!'

'My mind is made up. And you can consider yourselves lucky that you too are not being punished for defying Me.'

'Thank you, Lord. It wasn't our fault, honest! It was all Muriel's idea. We'll never defy You again. Personally, we'd rather have our legs ripped off and the bleeding stumps hammered up our nostrils than go to bed without any supper!'

He ignored their plaintive screeching and gazed searchingly at me. 'Now, Muriel, what do you have to say for yourself?'

'Ho-hum! It's past my bed time. Good night.'

With that I walked away.

'Oh, Muriel,' He shouted.

I stopped but did not turn to face Him.

'It occurred to Me earlier today that we could do with a bit more light around here, to help us see what we're doing. And so I decided, in My infinite wisdom, of which you may have heard Me speak occasionally, that tomorrow I will create a sun. Just a little idea of My own. Thought I'd let you know. Good night. Sleep tight. And don't forget to say your prayers.'

The next morning, after I'd done the washing up and scrubbed the kitchen floor, I joined the rest of the archangels outside. They were staring through the gloom, upwards and into the distance. I followed their gaze and after a few moments I could just make out the tiny figure of Himself, standing aloft one of the pointy things on top of the highest mountain.

As I watched I could just discern Him raising His arm and pointing into the murky blankness of the sky. And from that great distance we could barely hear a still small voice intoning:

Let there be light!

This was followed by the merest suggestion of

Clap!

Flash!

Puff!

'By Jiminy! He's done it one more time! No sooner had The Lord said, "Let there be light!", than there was light!'

Light there was, all around. Above us, in a sky which was now the deepest, purest azure, hung a burnished disc of gold, bathing us in its warm radiance, throwing its welcome rays across the face of Heaven, illuminating every crack and crevice and showing how grubby the bedroom curtains looked.

After a lot of hallelujahing from the others, we returned to our task, moving the mountains exactly 159 yards to the right. But now, because of the unaccustomed heat, we cast aside our frocks and worked stripped to our knickers and bras.

All day long we toiled. And at the end of it, muscles aching and limbs leaden with weariness, we fell gratefully into our beds.

Despite my exhaustion, sleep eluded me. After tossing and turning for an hour I could bear it no longer, so I raised my voice and shouted, 'Somebody forgot to turn the sun off!'

From a nearby room I could hear Him mumbling and grumbling to Himself, followed by the intonation...

'LET THERE BE NIGHT!'

The click of a finger...

CLAP!
FLASH!
PUFF!

And, lo! There was night.

Chapter Twelve

The Next 99,999,999,999 Years, Six Months And Twenty-Eight Days...

he next 99,999,999,999 years, six months and twenty-eight days passed slowly and boringly. Each morning we were up with the sun and after I'd done the washing up and scrubbed the kitchen floor I joined the others as we worked at shifting one of His latest creations from this point in the universe, to that point in the universe. And, when He wasn't satisfied that we'd put it in exactly the right position, we humped the bloody thing to yet another point in the universe.

On good days we'd just be shifting oceans and continents around, arranging and rearranging them according to His whim. On bad days we'd have to struggle to haul an entire galaxy halfway through space and back again. And when we finally got it into the position that suited His fastidious eye, He'd complain because one planet wasn't exactly and precisely aligned with another, or because one measly little asteroid had got chipped in the move.

And on every single one of these thirty-six thousand, five hundred million, eight hundred and seventeen days I thought of my encounter with Cesspit. But never once did I feel a 'stirring'. To add to my misery, the food became even worse, due to the fact that He had less time to do any cooking.

It must have been on the thirty-six thousand, five hundred million, eight hundred and fifteenth day – or was it the thirty-six thousand, five hundred million and sixteenth day? – I can't remember precisely as one was so like another. Except that on this particular day I had one of my ideas. It was an idea that made all of my other ideas seem like passing fancies.

I was working alone, pushing, I seem to recall, a minor planet called Hilda (damn stupid name for a planet, but when you've created the countless billions that He'd churned out, you tend to lose inspiration) from the outer extremity of the star system of Gavin Minor and into the orbit of the giant sun, Tiddles – where, according to Him, it would make a pleasing and amusing visual counterpoint to some dreary little moon He'd knocked out earlier – when I thought to myself, this is not the sort of work that an archangel should be doing.

I stopped for a moment to catch my breath. And it occurred to me that there must be a better way of getting a planet from one place to another without physically shoving it. So I hovered there, regarding Hilda, and wondered, just wondered whether...

I closed my eyes, took a deep breath, and intoned...

'LET THIS
BLOODY THING
BE MOVED!'

And I opened my eyes. And lo! The bloody thing had not moved. Oh well, it was just an idea. But wait a moment, hadn't I forgotten something?

I closed my eyes again, took another deep breath and reintoned:

'LET THIS
BLOODY THING·
BE MOVED!'

And this time I clicked my fingers.
And there was a *CLAP!* of thunder.
A *FLASH!* of lightning.
And a *PUFF!* of smoke.
Admittedly not quite such an impressive

CLAP!

or

FLASH!

or

PUFF!

as He achieved, but not bad for a beginner.

I opened my eyes and looked. And lo! No sooner had I said, 'Let this bloody thing be moved!', than the bloody thing was moved!

It was moved about eighteen inches. A trifle disappointing, but encouraging for an apprentice finger-clicker.

I spent all the rest of that day practising. By the end, I had not only succeeded in moving the planet across vast distances at will, but I'd also discovered I possessed the power to create things.

Nothing very impressive to start with, but I was still discovering the extent of my powers.

It began with me intoning:

'LET THERE BE...UM...LET ME THINK...WELL, ROCK!'

And lo! There was not rock. At least nothing that I recognized as a hard, stony, jagged thing that could be hurled at me.

Instead, there was the most appalling and unbearably loud noise in my ears which sounded as though a hundred trillion parakeets were having their livers pulled out through their backsides while at the same time shrieking, 'Yeah, baby, shake my love pump!,' to a tune that sounded vaguely similar

CREATION WORK SHEET

JOB Nº:	ARCHANGEL:	DAY:
790561116	Muriel	36,500,000,815

① wash dishes

② scrub K. floor

③ Move planet 'Hilda' (code 4727/P)
from creation depot into
orbit around sun 'Tiddles
(code 0028/S) of star system
'Gavin minor' — Place next to
moon third (3rd) out on the
left (code 9000167204/m) —
— see diagram....

Cesspit
Cesspit
Cesspit

moon
9000167204/m

X⁰

Hilda
goes here

other
moons

Tiddles

SIGNED:	CHECKED:
God	

to Raphael's 'Let's All Praise His Name'. I had to count that as a miserable failure.

Next I intoned:

'LET THERE BE SOMETHING TO DRINK THAT ISN'T NECTAR!'

And lo! there *was* something to drink that very definitely *wasn't* nectar. At that time I didn't know what it was, but it made me feel good, if slightly giddy, and the bubbles got up my nose.

With this feeling of elation, I became emboldened and started plucking words out of the air.

'LET THERE BE...ER...SPINACH!'

And lo! There was spinach. Tons and tons of the stuff, drifting round and round me, green and slimy and revolting to the tongue.

'LET THERE *NOT* BE SPINACH!'

And lo!, to my incredible relief, there was *not* spinach. In quick succession I created thermal underwear with reinforced gusset, cowpats and caviar, which looked remarkably like fish eggs and tasted rather less delicious than cowpats but considerably nicer than spinach.

Finally, as supper time approached, I became so emboldened by my success that I intoned:

'LET THERE BE "STIRRINGS"!'

But, alas, 'stirrings' there were not. I came to the regretful conclusion that I was not omnipotent. But comforted myself that I possessed abilities above and beyond those of the other archangels. Which made me the second most powerful being in the entire universe. This was to be my secret until such time as I could put my powers to good use.

I returned to Heaven, where they were just finishing supper.

'You're too late,' said Gabriel. 'We've eaten all the yummy nectar and ambrosia!'

'I'm not hungry, I ate earlier.'

'Pardon?'

'Er...when I say I ate earlier, what I mean is...um...'

But I was interrupted by Himself, who pushed back His chair, rapped on the table with His spoon and declared, 'Now listen carefully, I have something important to say. I've spent the last thirty-six thousand, five hundred million, eight hundred and fifteen – or possibly sixteen – days creating things of wonder and delight that I have scattered, with your help, hither and yon across the universe. My Really Triff And Absolutely Brill Plan is almost at an end.

'Only one last project remains. A project I shall start upon tomorrow. It will be My greatest feat of creation so far and I'm going to need all My strength so I'm off to bed. In the morning I start on The Big One!'

With that He strode out. Only to return a moment later.

'All right, own up, who's moved the stairs?'

Chapter Thirteen

t last we have reached the thirteenth chapter! And as thirteen is my very favourite number, I thought I'd take this opportunity to break off from my extraordinarily interesting and fascinating narrative and devote this part of the book to sharing with you the long list of my other very favourite things.

What I love more than anything are:

> 1. Slugs and snails and puppy dogs' tails. Preferably on toast. And washed down with Babycham, made, of course, from real[33]

33. Unfortunately, the rest of this chapter has been lost. In fact, it was eaten by the second editor (see Publisher's Warning on page 7). Although not ourselves superstitious, we feel that on this occasion the number...well, that number between twelve and fourteen...has proved unlucky for The Author. Not that we believe in such mumbo jumbo. We apologize for this omission. It will not occur again. Fingers crossed and touch wood.

Chapter Fourteen
The Big One

The next morning we all awoke bright-eyed and bushy-winged and gathered in the kitchen where Himself was to reveal The Big One. Standing on His box He addressed us, 'Having created the universe and all that is in it, I am now ready to embark on My masterpiece, the ultimate creation that will be the monument to My omnipotence. I am about to make the perfect planet – it will be the most beautiful I have yet designed, incorporating all the best bits of the other planets and yet going far, far further, for this one will have things that the others do not – things like assorted greengroceries and myriad life forms, ranging from the humblest creeping thing to the most sophisticated being in the entire universe, excepting us, of course.

'To prove My complete and utter omnipotence, I am going to undertake this enormous scheme without any assistance from you. I shall create this wondrous planet single-handed! Furthermore, and with all due modesty, to show that I am the most powerful Being in existence, I shall complete this vast endeavour in only six – count 'em – just six days!'

The others started running around, 'hallelujahing', praising His name and, secretly, jumping for joy at having a six-day holiday.

Having made His announcement, He changed into His overalls, jumped into His Chariot of Fire and roared off across the sky to commence His ultimate work.

That day – the first day of Earth's creation – passed pleasantly. The others lounged lazily around, doing nothing, and I, after I had clicked my fingers and completed the washing up and floor scrubbing, stole away privately to practise my new powers, conjuring many more amazing things out of thin air. Mostly amazing things that I could eat and drink.

I returned late to the shack, tired but happy and very, very full, to find the others moaning and groaning that there wasn't any supper and they'd had to make do with stale ambrosia sandwiches because Himself had not yet returned from His day's labours. They were in such a bad mood that they barely sang sixty desultory verses of 'Let's All Praise His Name Even Though He Hasn't Bothered To Make Our Dinner And Our Stomachs Feel Like Our Throats Have Been Cut' before deciding to call it a day and go to bed.

It was in the small hours of the morning that we were awakened by His voice. He summoned us into His bedroom and when we were all collected, He gave us a progress report on His efforts so far.

It seems that He had somewhat over-estimated His powers. After working all day and half the night, He had not fulfilled His schedule. In fact, all He had accomplished was to form a pleasingly globular planet which lacked certain of the elements He had designed – like continents, land masses, oceans and seas.

Beckoning us closer He whispered that, as He was somewhat late in His time-table, He was offering us the privilege of helping Him in His great work. But He swore us to secrecy, saying that we were never, ever to tell a soul that He had had help. This we promised solemnly to do, given that there wasn't another soul to tell, even if we'd wanted to.

He then drew out a list headed 'Things To Be Done'. The first item – 'Have Breakfast' – and the second, 'Make Nice Round Planet', were crossed off, but all of the other notes remained and the list stretched from there to eternity and back again.

He explained that He had reassessed the position and decided each of us was to play an important role. Gabriel was to be responsible for putting all the twiddly bits – like mountains, ravines and tundra – on the continents after He had formed them. Raphael was in charge of all stretches of water below the size of major oceans. Uriel would help with various greengrocery items including moss and lichens, the smaller and less gaudy flowers and the duller root vegetables. Zadkiel was to be second-in-command of life forms from amoeba up to and including, but not greater than, moths. Anything more spectacular would, of course, be left to Him. And I...I was to go behind them, cleaning, scrubbing, dusting, polishing and generally clearing up the mess they made.

Looking at the list, Gabriel said, 'While not wishing to question Your wisdom which, as we all know because You have frequently mentioned it – but not so frequently as to appear boastful, honest – is infinite, do You still think we'll be able to accomplish all this in only five days?'

He answered, 'I've thought of that. Tell Me, how many hours are there in a day?'

'Twenty-four,' we chorused.

'And which idiot arbitrarily decided that each day should contain only twenty-four hours?'

'You did!'

'Yes, well, I'm sure I had a good reason for it at the time. But now I am ordaining that each day will consist of four hundred and seventy-six hours, and that only three of them shall be night. That should be enough to get the job done. Now, I'm going upstairs for My three hours sleep, after which we'll start on the job in earnest.'

We reminded Him that there wasn't an upstairs and that He was already in His bedroom. He reminded us that He didn't need reminding about anything, being omniscient. So we said good-night and didn't dare remind Him to set His alarm clock.

Sixteen hours later He leapt from His bed and resumed the great enterprise. And thus did we create the Earth and all that's on it in only five days plus the one that He'd already wasted. Which were really ninety-nine days, taking into account that one of His new days equalled nineteen of His old days.[34]

Every day we toiled at our tasks. Or, rather, the others toiled while I went behind them, looking at the mess they'd left, clicking my fingers and saying, 'LET THERE NOT BE MESS!' And lo! there was *not* mess. This left me four hundred and seventy-five hours and fifty-five minutes a day to occupy myself as best I could.

The days passed peacefully until the fourth when, at about half past 227 o'clock in the afternoon, we heard a sound like thunder, which we knew wasn't thunder as we had not yet got around to creating weather, and therefore must be Himself having one of His tantrums. We dropped whatever we were doing – painful for Gabriel who was just fixing a large pointy thing to the top of Mont Blanc which crashed on his toe – and rushed (or, in Gabriel's case, hobbled) across the partially completed planet to join Him.

He was standing atop the highest mountain which we called Mount Duvet but which later became Everest and He said, 'I've just been making a tour of inspection and I'm not a happy God, not a happy God at all. Gabriel! You are responsible for putting all the twiddly bits on to the continents I've created. By and large I concede that you've done a good job, but will you explain to Me what that is yonder?'

Gabriel turned to look and said, 'That's a mountain.'

'It certainly looks like a mountain, but why is smoke pouring from the top of it?'

'I...er...d-don't kn-know,' Gabriel stammered, 'it wasn't like that when I last looked. It was just like any other mountain and it w-w-wasn't sp-sp-spewing smoke and rock and molten lava.'

'Which is pouring all over My beautiful clean glacier, causing it to melt and drip into My newly-created and perfectly-

34. We would just like to point out that we think it's a pretty amazing feat that God managed to create the Earth and all that's on it in ninety-nine days, even if He did have some assistance. In fact, absolutely and incredibly amazing considering how long it takes a plumber to turn up to fix a dripping tap.

formed Gobi desert. There's no point in having a desert if it's full of water. Muriel, go and clear it up before it turns into another swamp, of which we already have more than a sufficiency.'

Gabriel looked downcast and said, 'I'm very sorry, I suppose I must have got the ingredients mixed up.'

Himself then turned to Raphael, saying, 'You are in charge of all stretches of water below the size of major oceans, can you explain what's gone wrong with that one?'

Raphael looked at the small-ish sea in question and answered, 'It looks all right to me.'

'It may look all right but try tasting it.'

Raphael dipped in his finger and licked it. 'Grooh!', he yelped.

'Grooh, indeed! How much salt did you put in there?'

'Exactly the amount in the recipe You gave me – one heaped tablespoon for every hundred gallons.'

'Well, it tastes as though you poured an entire barrel into that. It's so salty that nothing will live in there.

'And speaking of living things, Uriel, you've been given the task of helping Me with the greengroceries, kindly tell me what this nasty little object is?'

'That?' said Uriel. 'Why, that's a mushroom.'

'Oh. Is it?'

'Yes, You remember, it was on Your list between Muscatel and Mustard.'

'Yes, yes, of course I remember. And I suppose this is a quite adequate...er...mushroom. It's just that I expected it to be, well, shinier. I'll overlook that for the moment and turn to Zadkiel who is second-in-command of life forms from amoeba up to and including, but not greater than, moths. Tell Me, Zadkiel, what is this?'

He opened His hand and revealed a small creature crawling across His palm. Zadkiel peered at it and said, 'That? Why, that's...er...um...a hippopotamus.'

'You're guessing, aren't you? That is not a hippopotamus, which resembles a "sofa" with teeth and which I finished creating not half-an-hour ago. So what is this?'

'Um...is it by any chance a bunny rabbit?'

'No it is not. A bunny rabbit is a fluffy furry creature with

a pom-pom tail and a little twitchy nose. While this, this...
THING, is small and wriggly and slimy and squirmy and
horrible! So what is it?'

'I don't know,' Zadkiel admitted woefully, 'but it's eating
that mushroom.'

And as we watched, the small, wriggly, slimy, squirmy,
horrible thing took a large bite out of the mushroom, swallowed, belched, rolled over and lay motionless on its back.

Chapter Fifteen
The Big Bang

hey stared at it in a stunned silence. Eventually, Himself said, 'What has happened to the small, wriggly, squirmy, slimy, horrible thing?' And I said, 'That thing is a slug. It ate the mushroom which isn't a mushroom but a toadstool and as a result it has poisoned itself and died.'

'Slug?' said Himself. 'What's a slug? I don't remember ordering anything called a slug. And what's this "toadstool"? I'm sure that wasn't on My list.'

'No,' I replied, 'neither of them were on Your list. I created them, along with the smoking mountain, which is a volcano, and the sea with too much salt in which nothing can live and which I call the Dead Sea.'

Again His voice was like thunder.

'You created them? You!'

'Yes, me!'

'How did you create these things?'

'The same way You do. I just close my eyes, think of a word, any word like, for example, "spider" and say "LET THERE BE SPIDER!" Then I click my fingers and...'

CLAP!
FLASH!
PUFF!

'Lawksamercy,' cried the archangels, 'Muriel can do it too! No sooner did he say, "Let there be spider!" than lo! there is...well...a nasty creepy-crawly thing with lots of hairy legs. And we don't like it!' They picked their skirts up and scuttled behind Himself for protection. Himself yielded not a step. He stood there, glaring at me.

'SO, MURIEL,' He thundered, 'YOU'VE FINALLY DIS-COVERED THAT YOU TOO POSSESS POWERS, BUT WHY ARE YOU USING THEM TO CREATE NASTY SQUIGGLY, SQUIRMY AND HAIRY-LEGGED THINGS?

WHY ARE YOU ABUSING YOUR GIFTS TO CREATE VOLCANOES, POISONOUS PLANTS AND OTHER ABOMI-NATIONS?'

'Everybody should have a hobby.'

'A HOBBY! YOU CALL PERVERTING AND DESPOILING MY GREATEST MASTERPIECE A HOBBY!'

'Well, it passes the time. And look at what You've created – fluffy little bunny rabbits and cuddly koalas, pretty flowers which waft scents. It's all so...so *bland*, I thought I'd create some things that were more interesting, more exciting, more dangerous! Things that would add a bit of spice to this depressingly bijou planet.'

He waxed wrathful, more wrathful than I had ever seen Him.

'YOU DARE TO IMPOSE YOUR IDEAS ON MY CREATION?'

'Why not? After all, I am as powerful as you.'

'NO ONE IS AS POWERFUL AS THE SUPREME BEING!'

'I am and I'll prove it. How would you like to be a toad?'

'I WARN YOU, MURIEL, BE VERY, VERY CAREFUL!'

I closed my eyes, took a very, very deep breath and intoned, 'LET HIM BE A TOAD!'

I clicked my fingers...

CLAP!

FLASH!

PUFF!

Slowly I opened my eyes. And lo! He was *not* a toad.

'Funny,' I said, 'it worked on that hippopotamus earlier. Do you mind if I have another try?'

'MURIEL! THIS IS THE END! YOU ARE FIRED!'

'Fired? You can't fire me! I've got my rights! What about my three months' notice and golden handshake?'

'OH, GO TO HELL!

'Hell? Where's Hell? Look, as I was saying, you can't fire me because...'

CLAP!

FLASH!

PUFF!

...I'm qu
  i
    i
      i
        i
          i
          i
            i
              i
                i
                  i
                    i
                      i
                        i
                          i
                            i
                              i
                                i
                                  i
                                    i
                                      i
                                        i
                                          i
                                            i
                                              i
                                                i
                                                  i
                                                    i
                                                      i
                                                        i
                                                          i
                                                            i
                                                              i
                                                                i
                                                                i
                                                                  i
                                                                    i
                                                                      i
                                                                        tting!'

97

Chapter Sixteen

Paradise Lost

hus was I hurled headlong flaming from th'ethereal sky and cast into the bottomless pit.[35]

I soon discovered that the pit wasn't bottomless when I hit the bottom of it with the top of me. When I regained consciousness I found myself in the darkest darkness I'd ever seen. Or not seen. I couldn't understand why it took my eyes so long to adjust to the stygian gloom, until I realized that I didn't have the light from my halo. Indeed, I didn't have a halo at all. And I didn't have a silly white frock either. Nor a huge flapping pair of plaid wings.

But I still had my fingers, so I said 'LET THERE BE LIGHT!', clicked them and a huge pillar of fire leapt in front of me. As the flames danced, spouted and licked into the air I could just make out a massive pair of adamantine gates.

---

35. This passage owes something to Milton's *Paradise Lost*. In fact, it owes everything to that epic poem. The Author claims it is a parody of Milton and directs us to his monograph, *Parodies Regained*.

Impaled on top of them was a grimacing skull, gaping in the rictus grin of one who has died in unimaginable torment. Under it hung a sign with words daubed in blood:-

> BEWARE!
> YOU ARE APPROACHING
> HADES
> *THE INFERNAL REGION.*
> ABANDON HOPE
> ALL YE WHO ENTER HERE.
> POPULATION: 0
> TWIN TOWN : BRUSSELS

Involuntarily a shiver ran down my spine, the hairs on the back of my head prickled and I felt my knees tremble. I turned away but was met by a wall of blank darkness. There was nowhere to go but forward. Fearfully, I walked towards the gates, my footsteps ringing hollow in the terrible dead silence. I came abreast of those huge, forbidding gates and pushed them with quivering hand.

At first they resisted my touch but then slowly, menacingly slowly, they yielded, swinging open with a mournful creaking groan. I crossed the threshold and entered the abyss. No sooner had I set foot on the other side of the gates than all Hell broke loose.

Where can I find the words to describe that sound? It was like nothing I'd ever heard. It seemed to come from deep within the maw of that fathomless darkness, rising, ever rising, in a thin, curdling shriek, at first utterly incomprehensible, assaulting my agonized ears.

I cowered beneath the awful sound, screaming, 'Which horrible hound of hell is this? Reveal yourself!'

Finally my tortured ears discerned the blood-chilling message: 'Hello! Prescott's the name, Rodney Prescott.'

From the nightmare darkness a grotesque apparition emerged, thrusting its deathly white hand towards me. Clutched in the skeletal fingers was a card. Fearfully I snatched it from the grisly claw.

RODNEY PRESCOTT

SENIOR PARTNER

ORDURE, ORDURE, FILTH, SLIME AND PRESCOTT

ESTATE AGENTS

'So you finally turned up,' he said, 'I've been waiting since the Thursday before Time Immemorial. Anyway, now you're here, let me give you a quick tour of the place. As you can see, it is a superior and highly desirable residence, set in millions of acres of rolling countryside and affording the most idyllic vistas on all sides. The main living (if it can be called living) area measures one hundred and forty-three thousand miles wide by two hundred and fifty-nine thousand miles long (that, of course, is into the bay window), having the benefit of fitted carpets throughout.

'This unique dwelling combines a wealth of original features plus the very latest in mod cons, including central heating, jacuzzi, integral garage, fitted wardrobes and kitchen units,

ESTATE AGENTS ORDURE, ORDURE, FILTH, SLIME & PRESCOTT.

OPEN
ESTATE
AGENT

bathroom en suite with low-level flush cistern and matching vanitory units in desirable avocado green.'

I cast around me. 'I can't see any of those things.'

'No, well, that's just estate agents' jargon. Or, to use the technical term, bare-faced lies. You haven't encountered lies before but you'll get used to them. To be brutally frank, it doesn't have any of those things. All right, the place doesn't look much but with a little flair, a good builder and extensive renovation and refurbishment it does have enormous potential. Given enough imagination and money, you could turn it into a cosy little purgatory.

'Look, why don't I leave you the keys and allow you to browse. Don't hurry, you've got all the time in the Underworld. Now, if you'll excuse me, I must rush, I understand there's shortly to be a boom in land sales on Earth – a lot of development in the suburbs of Eden – and I don't want to miss out.'

Before I could ask about the rateable value, main drains and closeness of bus routes, he had disappeared, leaving me alone. Utterly alone in this vast, desolate wasteland.

I had nothing – no status, no friends, no comfort. Nothing at all, except this derelict wilderness and a burning ache in my heart for revenge against He who had stripped me of everything and cast me into the loathsome void.

As I wandered, abandoned and solitary, through the echoing caverns of this inhospitable region I realized that for the very first time in my long existence I was happy!

Yes, ecstatically, deliriously happy!

I rushed back through the numberless chambers of Hell, back to those huge grim gates and ripped down the 'For Sale' notice.

Hades was mine!

It wasn't much of a place, but it was home. And I had plans for it.

Chapter Seventeen

Home Sweet Home

ooking back over the millennia it's difficult for me to remember exactly what Hades was like when I moved in. It has changed so much since then.

In those days it was just a little hell-hole, nothing fancy, but somewhere to hang my hate (as it were). Since then it has grown and expanded and improved to become what it is today – The Hades Leisure Park, incorporating The Hellfire Club and Inferno-A-Go-Go Disco (a wholly-owned subsidiary of Hellton Hotels Inc.).

Right from the start I intended to set up a rival attraction to Heaven. Somewhere that was not run, as He ran His place, like a boy scouts camp but somewhere you could, if you so wished, scout for camp boys, not to mention willing girls and every animal of every possible gender, all in a constant state of sexual arousal.

My kingdom was going to provide everything that His did not, which left a lot of scope considering that Heaven offers very little apart from infinite harp recitals. You need the patience of a saint to endure it, which explains why it is populated almost entirely by saints and some of the duller popes and prelates who didn't have the imagination to try The Seven Delightful Sins before condemning them. (Mind you, we can boast more than our fair share of pontiffs down here, especially those from the heydays of the Middle Ages when they spread their message of brotherly love in more physical ways. Not to mention sisterly love and, indeed, love with people outside their immediate family circle. Pontiffs like Pope Urbane who could do things with a Papal Bull that surprised even me. And absolutely astonished the beast in question.)

It must be some measure of our success that The Great Fraud and His followers have spent so much effort spreading lies and propaganda about my little enterprise. All that nonsense about thumbscrews, racks and red-hot pokers!

Certainly we have them, but only for those whose taste runs to such pleasures. If you don't relish torture – either receiving or inflicting it – nobody is going to force you. (Well, all right, old Sacher de Masoch might try to force you, but that's just his way. If you don't want to play, simply knee him in the groin. He adores it. And when he begs and pleads for more, emulate de Sade: watch him squirm and grovel and absolutely refuse to pander to his needs. The Marquis really has raised cruelty to a peak of sophistication.)

We realize not everyone wants to gouge out the eyes or flay the flesh of his fellow man. Some prefer to do it to dumb animals, and who are we to say they are wrong? (Incidentally, I'm reliably informed that such pratices are common on Earth under the pretence of medical research. Naturally, this sort of behaviour does not appeal to the animal lovers among us who prefer dumb creatures to perform experiments on them, particularly stallions and German shepherds. The dogs, that is, not the human variety who remain faithful to their sheep.)

If, for some bizarre and squeamish reason, you do not wish to participate in these pleasant diversions, there are so many other ways to pass Infinity. For example, there is Pro-Am Pillaging and Looting in which you are invited to lay waste to large tracts of countryside under the tutelage of Genghis Khan. (Regrettably, ravishing has been dropped from this event due to an unfortunate and acutely embarrassing personal problem which I won't specify. Let's just say that not for nothing is he known as Genghis Khan't.)

Also on offer is Celebrity Plundering in which you can ransack entire cities under the supervision of royalty among who we are proud to list 'Mad' King Ludwig of Bavaria, 'Insane' Prince Francis of Ruthenia and 'Completely Loony' Duke Darren of Walloonia who is under the impression that he is a chipolata.[36]

Fortunately, being a six-foot cocktail sausage doesn't prevent Darren from plundering with the best of them. And probably the very best of them is dear old Ivan the Terrible, one of the all-time great plunderers who got his nickname for much the same reason as Genghis got his. (Ask Catherine the Great why Ivan is Terrible. And ask any of our several million clients who have shared her bed why Catherine is Great.) But enough of Ivan's shortcomings – so to speak – they are more than compensated for by the rampant satyrism of his son, Ivan the Amazing, and nephew Ivan the Really Brain-Explodingly Fantastic.[37]

There are so many ways in which you can while away your time and when, after a long day, you return tired, happy and gore-spattered after some enthusiastic Synchronized Vandalism (desecrate churches and deface the world's greatest works of art to your favourite Nazi marches under the tuition of a qualified Visigoth, packed lunch included), you'll probably want to soothe away the cares of the day in a relaxing hot bloodbath, gorge yourself to bursting in one of our many restaurants (one to suit every palate from vegan, where only the freshest vegetables are eaten, to cannibal where only the freshest vegans are eaten) and curl up for a few hours with a really bad book. We have the largest library of erotica in the universe, not to mention an unparalleled selection of pornographic films and videos, showing sexual acts that will make the eyes pop out of your head.

36. Among our clients Ludwig is also known as the 'Mad' Queen of Bavaria, due to his fondness for our male members. And, indeed, all male members whether or not they belong to patrons of our club.

37. Not to be confused with his identical twin brother, Igor the So-So. Although many of our female clients have confused them and been very disappointed as a result.

And so to bed. Where you can bonk yourself brainless with one of the great courtesans or legendary studs of history. Or both. And perform sexual acts that will make the eyes pop out of your head. Literally.

But what if you become bored rigid by being bored rigid (as we amusingly put it)? No problem! There are so many other entertainments to divert you.

If you wish for a quiet, contemplative evening you could play Diabolic Scrabble (only obscene words accepted) with Machiavelli but, be warned, he cheats. Or join the art class where you'll be taught how to forge some of the world's greatest masterpieces, to be destroyed the next day by the Synchronized Vandals. Or you can just retire to the Smoking Room (next to the Smouldering Room and along the corridor from the Bursting Into Flames Room – no ladies admitted since one was singed by a masochist who set fire to himself; she caused the most terrible fuss – Hell hath no fury like a woman scorched) and enjoy a Bloody Mary, or the non-alcoholic version, a Bloody Tee-Totaller, made from a freshly-slaughtered Mary and Tee-Totaller respectively. As you sip your favourite tipple you can browse through *Helle* magazine to discover what the well-dressed thrill-seeker is wearing, or, rather, having ripped off their willing body this season. Or you can put your feet up on a poof and watch hellevision which keeps you in touch with news of the upper world's latest disasters, catastrophes and holocausts. Or, as we call them, our latest triumphs.

Which other leisure complex in this or any other world could offer you all this? And for so little!

Yes, all this can be yours.

To enjoy the infinite and exquisite pleasures offered by Hades all you have to do is sell me your soul! What a bargain! And to make it even more convenient, I'll buy it on easy terms, stretched over the rest of your life.[38]

38. This offer does not apply to Mrs Elspeth Jenkins, Mr Zigismund Kowalski, Han Wen Yoo, Abdullah Al Akram or The Very Reverend Maurice Gilchrist who, unfortunately, have left it too late. Exactly one minute too late. Goodbye! However, you, Dear Reader, may like to fill in the membership form at the end of this chapter. Assuming, of course, you are not one of the above named.

As I always say, for most things you need Hire Purchase, but to enter the Underworld we offer Lower Purchase! People have been known to die laughing at that joke. And those who don't laugh just die, screaming in agony.

Oh, by the way, this business about the Fiery Furnace. Don't believe everything you hear. Admittedly, it does exist, but it's just a form of central heating like any other. We switched years ago from fuelling it with Souls in Torment. Today we simply shovel in advertising executives. What we describe as a blaze of publicity!

Well, that's given you a peek into Hades as it is in the twentieth century. It is, I'm sure you'll agree, one Hell of a place. So very, very different from the empty, echoing hulk that I inhabited all those eons ago. And what made the difference and started me on my long and highly successful career was my brilliantly simple coup of persuading my first client to eat an apple.

HADES LEISURE PARK

Please enrol me as an After-Life Member of The Hades Leisure Park (incorporating The Hellfire Club and Inferno-A-Go-Go Disco), the premier pleasure complex of this and every other world.

I understand that in exchange for my eternal soul I can enjoy the myriad facilities, perversities and indulgences of The Ultimate Pleasure Dome for the rest of Infinity (or until Armageddon, whichever is sooner.)

I also understand that as soon as my application is accepted The Hades Leisure Park will rush me a FREE GIFT of six bottles of vintage Brimstone.

HOTELS!

HELLFIRE CLUB

PRO-AM PILLAGING

CATHERINE THE GREAT!

DISORDER FORM

Surname ....
   (Mr/Mrs/Miss/Ms/Other : Delete according to gender, marital status, life form)
Anti-Christian names (in full) ....
   Address: House Name or Number ....
     Town/City ....
     Zip or Postcode ....
     Country ....
     Planet ....
     Galaxy ....
     Universe ....

   Signature: ....
   (Beasts make mark here): ....

Complete this coupon and rush it to:
Hades Leisure Park, p.l.c.,
P.O. Box 666
Underworld.
As a member of The Hades Leisure Park I agree not to abide by any of the rules of the club.

MONEY BACK GUARANTEE
If not entirely satisfied with the facilities of Hades within 7 millennia we guarantee that we will not give your money back.

Chapter Eighteen
Nipples Like Ripe Apricots

After being dumped in Hades, I wandered around my new domain. As I surveyed it, I realized how much needed to be done. The place was in shabby condition, it had been left empty and neglected since The Year Dot and was in need of a great deal of work.[39]

Water dripped down the walls, the wind howled through the roofs, paint flaked and peeled from every surface, fungi sprouted from each crack and the place was pervaded by the sour, rank stench of decay. Looking around, I realized it just wouldn't do. It was far too cosy.

I spent a lot of time making it as squalid and sordid as possible, covering the walls with slime, the floors with sewage and hanging the windows with festoons of rotting entrails. That done, I had mains sulphur piped in to waft its noxious fumes through the chambers.

When I'd finished Hades was the sort of place that would strike dread even into the black hearts of the desperate and despised, the murderous and mad, the vicious and vile who were to be my clients. But when they eventually arrived, they felt instantly at home and kept pestering to know what had happened to the 7.43. I had, quite unwittingly, modelled it on a railway waiting-room.[40]

But my first customers wouldn't arrive for some considerable time (and the train never arrived at all, that's the hell of the place) because there were no customers available except for His archangels and I knew there was no point in trying to tempt them to join me, especially since He'd offered them a whole bundle of incentives to retain their loyalty – including pension scheme, Luncheon Vouchers and company chariots. This narrowed down my potential clientele considerably.

I could barely contain my desire to start on my diabolic career of seducing souls and so, in between re-desecrating Hades, I would pop up to Earth for a recce, to spy out the land and see how His creation was progressing. Obviously, I couldn't just wander around the place in my usual form, but it was

39. The Year Dot. Short for The Year Dorothy. Before years were numbered, they were given individual names, which were frequently shortened. The Year Dot was the first, followed by The Year Doug, The Year Dick and The Year Ken. The system had its disadvantages beause people had trouble remembering whether The Year George came before or after The Year Mimi and whether that was preceded or succeeded by The Year Rupert. This method was abandoned in The Year Fiona (or possibly Gerald). It was replaced by a numbering system – The Year Dot became 1, Doug was 2, Dick 3 and so on. However, the numbers weren't actually called one, two, three, etc. As the counting system was based on digits of the hand, the numbering went Thumb, Finger Next To Thumb, Middle Finger and so on through the fingers of both hands. Having run out of fingers, the 11th year was known as Big Toe, the 12th was The Not-Quite-Such-A-Big-Toe Next to Big Toe and so on up to The Little Teeny Weeny Toe On The Left Foot which was 20. This proved moderately satisfactory until New Year's Eve of The Little Teeny Weeny Toe On The Left Foot when it was realized that they had virtually run out of extremities. Thus the 21st year became known as The Sticky-Out Thing That Boys Have But Ladies Don't. After this the system broke down completely and was, in turn, replaced with the one we now recognize.

40. It was after this discovery that I completely re-decorated Hades, turning it into the luxuriously-appointed recreation centre and leisure complex that it now is. However, I've retained one corner of it in the old style for those deeply perverse clients who get their masochistic kicks from waiting for eternity for a train that never arrives. It's next to The Pub With No Beer and just behind The Restaurant That Is Fully Booked Until The End Of Time And Even If It Wasn't, We Wouldn't Admit Riff-Raff Like You.

surprisingly easy to disguise myself and pass unnoticed. They were far too busy to pay any heed to an extra stone lying on the beach or a log that suddenly appeared on the ground.

In these guises I would lurk, watching and waiting for the first signs of some life form that was worth tempting and, when I got bored with trying to seduce sticks, leaves and plankton into the ways of wickedness, I would do a little freelance creating of my own. I derived quite a bit of pleasure from hearing one or other of the archangels letting out a scream and shrieking, 'Euggghhh! Who put these disgusting leathery wings on this mouse? And why is it sucking the blood out of that dear little antelope I spent all yesterday afternoon creating?' Or, 'Which idiot took all the legs off this lizard? And whose idea was it to put this rattle on its tail?'

At night I'd skulk outside the shack disguised as a shrub, eavesdropping on their conversation to discover what effects my latest creations had had.

'Gabriel,' Raphael would say, 'you know that nice black and white animal I made that looks a bit like a badger but isn't? Well, guess what? Today I went to inspect it to see if its fur was sticking snugly to its body and when I approached it, it gave off this most appalling pong. It really stank! I'm sure that smelling like a rancid herring wasn't in the original blueprint.'

And Gabriel would reply, 'You think you've got trouble! I've just been combing my silky golden hair and look what I've found – there are millions of little white scaly bits in it! Look, the stuff is all over my nice clean frock.'

And Uriel would chime in, 'Attisshoo! Oh! I'b hab dem for days. Dat's nobbing combared wid habing you dose bunged ub and consdandly sneeding. Attisshoo! I feel like death warbed ub.'

And Zadkiel would pause for a moment from squeezing the pus out of the boils that had so suddenly and inexplicably erupted on his face and say, 'You know, this place isn't entirely turning out as I expected. But I suppose when you're doing a job this big, you've got to expect the odd hiccup.'

And Raphael would say, 'Hic! What's a hic-hic-hiccup? And hic has any-hic-body got a cure for whatever it hic is that keeps making me go hic?'

Himself noticed nothing amiss because He was too intent on the other side of Earth creating His masterwork. He called it Eden and He was fashioning it single-handedly, moulding and shaping it to become the most beautiful place He had ever created. It was a riot of multi-coloured blooms and succulent fruits, of dancing fountains and lush verdant palms. The leaves sparkled in the constant sunlight, dappling the paths beneath. The breeze sighed and riffled, gently stirring the limpid water of the pools where brightly-coloured carp rose to splash the rippled surface. Here a lamb gambolled giddily, there a fawn frisked and frolicked while nearby a kitten skittered through the orchids; above it a turtle dove cooed and a nightingale warbled its liquid notes into the scented sky.

It was a feast for the eyes, a symphony for the ears, a bouquet for the nostrils and a joy for the heart. It was, in short, utterly repellent.

But under the watchful eyes of Himself there was little I could do to exercise my demonic powers, except smuggle in the odd aphid, weevil and thrip to munch His roses. And the occasional mole to flaw His perfect lawns.

Instead I bided my time, watching and waiting until the moment I could fulfil my destiny. And that moment came at exactly 238 o'clock in the afternoon of the fifth day when He called His archangels to Him. They came running from all corners of the planet and gathered about Him in the middle of Eden. He ordered them to sit on a nearby log while He revealed His final and ultimate intention.

And so it was that as they sat – and as I groaned silently under their weight – He declared unto them: 'I am now ready to perform My final and greatest act of creation. Yea, even though I have already created a myriad profusion of breathtaking wonders entirely single-handed, except for a little help with the menial chores that we need not mention outside this circle, this last creation will make them seem like cheap conjuring tricks. The time has come for me to fashion a creature called Man, which I will create in My image, after My likeness.'

So saying, He stooped to the ground and scooped together a handful of dust. The archangels, entranced and trembling with anticipation, leaned forward to gaze at the little mound.

'From this meagre dust will spring the acme of My creation.'

He closed His eyes, drew in His breath and intoned:

'LET THIS DUST BE MAN. AND LET THIS MAN BE MADE IN MY IMAGE, AFTER MY LIKENESS!'

CLAP!

FLASH!

AT-TISSHOOOO!

A still, small voice said, 'I'b terridly soddy.'

'URIEL! YOU'VE BLOWN AWAY MY GREATEST CREATION! HOW MANY TIMES HAVE I COMMANDED YOU, IF YOU'RE GOING TO SNEEZE, USE A HANDKER-CHIEF?'

'Neber. You neber told be dat.'

'NO, WELL, IT NEVER SEEMED IMPORTANT BEFORE. NOW, IF YOU CAN CONTROL YOUR NOSTRILS, I WILL START ALL OVER AGAIN. AND THIS TIME I REQUIRE COMPLETE SILENCE!'

Once more He stooped. Once more He scooped together a handful of dust. Once more He closed His eyes and drew in His breath. And once more He intoned:

'LET THIS DUST BE MAN. AND LET THIS MAN BE MADE IN MY IMAGE, AFTER MY LIKENESS!'

CLAP!
FLASH!
PUFF!

Chapter Nineteen

Quivering Buttocks[41]

When the smoke had cleared, the archangels leaned forward again and gazed at His final creation. As one they raised their voices and exulted: 'We just don't believe this, even though we've seen it with our own eyes! No sooner did God say, "LET THIS DUST BE MAN" than, lo! this dust *was* man!

'And not only that, but no sooner did God say, "AND LET THIS MAN BE MADE IN MY IMAGE, AFTER MY LIKE-NESS!" than, lo!, he *was* made after His image, after His likeness! For lo!, this man is only five feet two inches tall and is wearing a bright orange wig!'

Thus was Adam created.

---

41. The publishers would like to apologize for the misleading titles of the last two chapters. Chapter Nineteen should have been headed 'Eden' and not 'Nipples Like Ripe Apricots'. This chapter should be titled 'Adam', and not as printed above. These changes were made at the last moment by The Author for his own nefarious purposes. We are confident that no other such amendments have crept into the silky blonde triangle of her tantalizing pubic mound.

And Himself raised Adam up to his feet. And Adam put one foot in front of the other and took his first halting steps on Earth. He walked straight into a palm tree, turned, tripped over a stone and fell headlong into a limpid pool. Himself dragged Adam from the water, raised him to his feet again but this time adjusted his wig so that it was not on back to front and so Adam could see where he was going. He blinked in the light and took his first look at Eden. He gazed around him at the riotous profusion of blooms and fruits, at the dancing fountains, the gambolling lamb, the frolicking fawn, at the cooing turtle dove and the warbling nightingale. He drank all this in, then he opened his mouth and uttered his first words on Earth: 'I'm bursting for a pee.'

Then he urinated over the orchids.

Himself turned to the archangels and spake unto them, saying, 'I think I've made a terrible mistake.' He then drew them to Him and said, 'I know I said that the creation of Man was to be My final act of creation, but looking at this shambling moron, I think I'll have one more try.'

So saying, He lightly flicked Adam on the back of the head with His finger, causing his wig to fly off and his body to slump to the ground in a coma. As Adam lay there, Himself plucked a rib from his body and held it aloft, saying, 'Behold I have plucked this rib from Adam.'

And Gabriel said, 'Behold He has plucked a rib. Um...can you eat it?'

And Himself said, 'As a matter of fact, you can. It's delicious with barbecue sauce.'

So they made a fire, cooked the rib and ate it.

Then Himself leant over Adam again and plucked another rib, saying, 'He'll never miss it.'

He held the second rib aloft, saying, 'Behold this other rib I have plucked from Adam. From this I will fashion My final and My greatest creation. From this will I fashion Woman.'

He closed His eyes, drew in His breath and intoned:
'LET THIS RIB BE WOMAN!'

CLAP!
FLASH!

'Hang on! Wait a second! I haven't finished yet!
'LET THIS RIB BE WOMAN. AND LET HER *NOT* BE MADE IN MY IMAGE, AFTER MY LIKENESS!'

PUFF!

And when the smoke cleared, the archangels exulted once more, chanting, 'Hallelujah! No sooner did God say, "LET THIS RIB BE WOMAN AND LET HER *NOT* BE MADE IN MY IMAGE, AFTER MY LIKENESS" than lo!, there *was* woman and she is most definitely and decidedly *not* made in His image, in His likeness!'

'Behold!', quoth Gabriel, 'her stature; she must be well over six feet tall!'

'Behold!', quoth Raphael, 'her fine blonde hair which is like unto spun gold!'

'Behold!', quoth Uriel, 'the alabaster whiteness and lustrous sheen of her silken skin!'

'Behold!' quoth Zadkiel, 'the enormous pair of knockers on her!'

And I did behold her and saw that she was tall and blonde and creamy-skinned and had an enormous pair of knockers. And I felt a 'stirring'. A 'stirring' such as I'd never felt before. And as I gazed at the perfection that was Eve, I felt an overwhelming desire, a desire to seduce this exquisite creature. As I stared into her cornflower blue eyes, I knew I had met my destiny.

My reverie was ruined by the sound of four archangels' bums crashing to the ground. 'Blimey!', said Gabriel, 'I could have sworn this log just stirred.'

Chapter Twenty
Rude Bits[42]

imself extended His hand to Eve and gently led her to the recumbent form of Adam, who lay on the ground, snoring loudly and scratching his groin. Himself blew in Adam's ear to wake him. When that had no effect, He shook his shoulder. Eventually, He managed to wake the Man by kicking him hard in the ribs.

'OWWWWWWW! That bloody well hurt!' He clutched his sides, saying, 'I don't know what was going on while I was asleep, but I feel completely plucked.'

And Himself presented Eve to Adam saying, 'This woman have I created to be your helpmeet and soulmate, your comfort and your wife. You shall cleave unto your wife and you shall be one flesh.'

And Adam replied, saying, 'Cut out all the poncey talk. I

---

42. We apologize for this chapter heading. This is obviously another attempt by The Author to create mischief and to mislead the reader. This chapter should be titled, 'Adam And Eve'.

didn't understand half of that but I will say one thing, this Eve's got a nice pair of knockers on her.'

Eve smiled sweetly and in a voice like molten honey crooned, 'I shall be your helpmeet and soulmate, your comfort and your wife. I shall cleave unto you and we shall be one flesh.'

And Adam smiled at Eve, saying, 'And I shall cleave unto you and we shall be one flesh. Now, what do you say to a quick leg-over?'

Himself said, 'Verily, I have created vegetables with a greater intellectual capacity than this gibbering dimwit. Desist this babbling and come with Me as I show you the glories of My creation which I have fashioned just for you.'

Eve took Adam's hand in hers and they walked slowly side by side through Eden, pausing now and again for her to admire the beauty that surrounded them and for him to urinate over it.

Finally, God led them to a secluded arbour and there He showed them a tree. He spake unto them, saying, 'Of every tree of the garden thou mayest freely eat. But thou shalt *not* eat of the fruit of this tree.'

And Adam said, 'Come again?'

So Himself spake again, 'Look, you cabbage-brained cretin, it's quite simple. You can stuff yourself on the fruit of that tree there, you can gorge yourself till you're sick on the fruit of that tree over there. But you cannot and must not lay one finger on the apples from this tree here. Got it? Savvy? Comprenez?'

'All right, I've got it. But what's so special about this tree? Looks the same as all the rest to me.'

'This is The Tree of Good and Evil and I, The Lord Thy God, forbid you to eat its fruit.'

'Fair enough. You're the boss and if You want to save the best fruit for Yourself, I s'pose You're entitled to. But there's no need to spin this fairy tale about The Tree Of Good and Evil. I wasn't born yesterday, you know.'

'Indeed you were not. You were born this very day and it's still not too late for Me to change My mind about your continued existence.'

But Eve soothed Him. 'We understand what You have said and we will obey Your command. Thank You for creating this beautiful place which we will cherish and nurture so that it will further glorify Your name.'

And Himself patted her hand and grinned stupidly, saying, 'Thank you, my dear, you've made an old God very happy. Now, I'm going to run along and leave you two young things alone. Why don't you be fruitful and multiply?' With that He winked at Eve, nudged Adam in the ribs, causing him to howl in pain, and disappeared.

When He'd gone, Adam turned to Eve and said, 'Well, you heard what He said, so let's get on with it! On your back, Woman, and brace yourself for a rattling good shag.'

And Eve spoke gently unto him, saying, 'I shall be your helpmeet and soulmate, your comfort and your wife. I shall cleave unto you and we shall be one flesh. But there will be no cleaving until you take that bloody stupid wig off.'

And all the while I pondered on His words regarding the apples on the tree, thinking that I had finally found the way to get my revenge on Him. My mind full of my plans, I left the Garden of Eden. But not before I'd watched Adam and Eve cleaving like rats up a drainpipe.

It was without doubt the most fun a log has ever had.[43]

43. We apologize for our apology at the beginning of the chapter. Having read these pages we now realize the title, 'Rude Bits', was an apt and accurate description of the subject matter contained herein. A bit saucy, wasn't it? We would further like make an apology to any reader who found the subject matter of this chapter offensive. We are very, very sorry – you must lead an incredibly dull life.

Chapter Twenty-One
The Temptation of Eve

A good deal of nonsense has been written about my first great success. All this balderdash about me taking the form of a serpent, sidling up to Eve and hissing, 'Pssst! Wanna nibble my Cox?'

Complete fantasy, like so much in 'The Bible'. No self-respecting demon would conduct a temptation like that. Can you imagine the effect that a talking snake would have on a sensitive young woman? Scare her witless and have her running in the opposite direction, completely defeating the object of the exercise.

To be a great tempter you need to use psychology. First, you have to work out what you want to achieve. And then you contrive a simple but elegant plan to ensnare your victim.

In this case the object was to persuade Eve to take, eat and share the forbidden fruit with Adam. So what was the most natural and least suspicious way in which I could offer Eve an apple?

Exactly!

And so it came to pass that I set up my stall in Eden, posing as a Greengrocer and High Class Fruiterer. And a dashed good-looking one at that.

Basic psychology. After being cleaved round the clock by that short-arsed, bald-headed, turnip-brained, sex-crazed lout, she was only too ready to be tempted into accepting the gift of a juicy, rose-red apple from a handsome, suave charmer with a debonair moustache, roguish grin and twinkling eye.

It was as simple as that. Of course, I may also have casually mentioned that after eating the apple Adam would experience a severe limpness in the cleaving department.

Eve went skipping off to share her apple and I quietly left the Garden of Eden, pausing only to trample His hollyhocks.

Chapter Twenty-Two
The Cain Mutiny

not even I realized just how easy it would be to alter the entire course of Himself's plans. The work of a few moments wrecked a millennium of His work. I knew He would be cross, but I little realized just how monumentally furious He would get over one small apple. His wrath was terrible to see. As soon as He learned of Adam and Eve's disobedience, He evicted them from Eden and forced them to wander, naked and alone, through the Earth, facing the terrors of the wilderness and the threats from ravening beasts, with nothing to comfort them except marathon cleaving sessions which were not much of a comfort for Eve who found she was increasingly suffering from headaches.

Things were pretty quiet, especially for me having only two people to tempt. This was proving futile as Eve was deaf to my blandishments, having sworn never, ever to talk to a stranger again. Adam was no better because only one thing tempted him and although I'm not noted for my squeamishness, even I drew the line at having carnal knowledge of someone who possessed all the charm, sensitivity and comeliness of a festering boil.

Unfortunately for her, Eve could not afford to be so choosy and so, despite a headache that lasted three years and seventeen days, the inevitable happened and she became pregnant.

Their first-born was Cain. As soon as I saw him I thought he was a promising little fellow and before he was toddling I was working on him, tempting him in every way I knew. Sadly without success. I couldn't persuade him to theft, as there was nothing in the world worth stealing. He was too young for adultery, even if Eve had been willing, which she wasn't because Cain was the spitting image of his father.

However, I did manage to get him to tell the odd lie – he would occasionally go up to Adam and say, 'Guess what, Dad! This morning I invented the wheel!'. When Adam asked what a wheel was and whether he could cleave the arse off it, Cain would say, 'I don't know! I was just making it up!' and run off chuckling to himself at his own naughtiness. It wasn't much – hardly the sort of transgression that would incur the wrath of Old Sourpuss Upstairs – but it was a start and I had high hopes for his future career.

These hopes were realized when, despite a headache lasting six years, five months and twelve days, Eve gave birth to her second son, Abel.

Cain didn't like Abel much because the younger boy was taller than him, had a full head of hair and had inherited his mother's good looks and gentility. He infuriated Cain by his fastidiousness in refusing to wear a goat's skin around him until it had first been separated from the goat.

One day, after Abel had been particularly prissy and complained about Cain urinating over some potatoes which, he said, was unhygienic, especially while he was eating them, Cain stormed off.

I found him sitting alone and, assuming the form of an itinerant Second-Hand Bits Of Wood Salesman, engaged him in conversation about the comparative merits of a large bit of wood with only one careful owner over a slightly bigger but cheaper bit of wood which had, admittedly, seen a certain amount of wear and tear.

After a lengthy debate, we agreed that the slightly bigger but cheaper bit of wood was, all things considered, preferable. We then haggled about the price until I allowed him to beat

PRIDE

ANGER

ENVY

LUST

GLUTTONY

GREED

SLOTH

???

me down to fifteen pebbles and a gerbil's jawbone. An incredible bargain, especially as I also agreed to take a twig in part exchange, but sometimes the end justifies the means.

Having concluded the deal, Cain went off, proudly cradling his new possession. Only to return a few minutes later, saying, 'Um. This large bit of wood I've just bought...what am I supposed to do with it?'

I explained to him that the bit of wood had magical properties and if used correctly would stop his brother criticizing him for his little foibles, like, for example, his habit of grabbing Abel by his testicles and squeezing them with all his might, which was the world's first and, at that time, only sporting activity.

'So,' he asked, 'how do I make this happen?'

'You simply take this large bit of wood and tap your brother on the head with it.'

'And what does that do?'

'If you tap hard enough, it...well, basically, it kills him.'

'Fine!'

Off he went again, humming happily.

A few minutes later he was back, saying, 'What exactly does "kills" mean?'

But by then I was no more than the merest wisp of sulphurous smoke.

Thus Abel became the world's first corpse. Cain became the world's first murderer. And Adam became the first person to fail to solve a whodunnit, lacking the intelligence to work out the culprit from a list of three suspects. Even when two of them had cast-iron alibis being, as he and Eve were, otherwise engaged in cleaving.

Cain's action enraged Old Misery Guts Upstairs who exiled him, forcing him to wander the desolate realms of Earth, searching in vain for a shrewd lawyer who could argue his innocence by proving that Abel had killed himself by repeatedly smashing his head against Cain's bit of wood.

It's doubtful that any lawyer, however sharp, could have convinced Himself that Abel was the world's first suicide. That record belongs to another of Adam's offspring, Clut, who I tempted into self-destruction by persuading him to jump from the top of a thousand-foot cliff, assuring him that the rocks below would break his fall. This was more difficult than I anticipated because I had trouble convincing Clut that when his body struck the rocks, it wouldn't do them any damage.

In the meantime Cain roamed the Earth for several hundred years until it finally dawned on Him that his quest for a lawyer was futile because even if he found one, he couldn't afford to pay him. This discovery caused him to lose the will to live.

I was more than pleased to welcome him as my very first client in Hades, where he has bided ever since, basking in the status of being our oldest and probably stupidest resident, with the exception of his brother Clut who is still full of remorse and tells anyone who listens, 'I can't forgive myself for making those lovely rocks all dirty with my blood.'

Since Cain's arrival we have been joined by countless billions more members, millions of whom have imitated and improved on his pioneering technique and who would willingly exercise them on Clut if only there was death after death.

Chapter Twenty-Three

The Dance of Death
Or
Apocalypso Now!

'm not one to boast, but within a very short space of time and at the expenditure of almost no effort, I had contrived the exile of Mankind from paradise and introduced murder.[44]

After that the going was easy. No sooner did Adam and Eve spawn a child than I tempted it to some new and delightful sin. For example, it was I who taught Onan the habit named after him.[45]

It was I who preached brotherly love. And sisterly love. Not to mention brotherly-in-law love and cousinly-once-removed love. It was I who encouraged Man to love his neighbour, especially when the neighbour's wife was out, experiencing total-strangerly love with whomsoever she happened to pick up. It was I who introduced the descendants of Adam to what

---

44. I'm lying again. I am, of course, one to boast. I even boast about my boastfulness. I am indubitably the most boastful being who has ever lived and that's being modest. Incredibly modest. In fact, I'm being so modest, I feel like boasting about it. But my incalculable and unequalled modesty prevents me.

Himself called the Seven Deadly Sins. I doubt whether anyone has ever enjoyed such job satisfaction.[46]

My successes were rapid and spectacular. As the world became populous, I rushed hither and thither, tempting, seducing, perverting and recruiting. Soon Hades was filling up with willing helpers, each of whom I sent out to spread my word and do my bidding, netting shoals of souls, diverting them from the straight and narrow, down the corkscrew path to my infernal realm.[47]

At this time, I reckoned I was claiming ten souls for every one who signed with Him. And as these members flocked to me, what did He do? He took to the bottle and drank Himself into an alcoholic daze lasting several thousand years.

As He slumbered in His drunken coma, Gabriel and the other archangels tried to staunch the flow of my subscribers

45. Onan's sin was self-abuse. He used to hurl insults at himself, shouting, 'I'm a deaf, blind, stunted, hairy-palmed tosser!' He believed himself to be completely insane, and blamed the condition on his new-found habit of spilling his seed on the ground. He was, in fact, completely insane but the cause of it was not self-gratification, but being dropped on his head by his brother, Er, who used the infant Onan as a ball which he kicked to his twin brother, Um.

   Er and Um were so called because when asked what names he would give them their father, Judah, an indecisive man, answered, 'Er… um…'. Yet another child was named Dunno for the same reason.

   Publisher's Note: This version does not coincide with that found in Genesis 38: 9, which states that Judah had only two sons: Er and Onan. Either we are privy to new and important information or The Author is lying through his teeth. We leave the reader to decide.

   A Doctor adds: 'There is no medical evidence to prove that Onanism makes you blind, deaf, hairy-palmed or stunts your growth. It certainly won't cause insanity. I practised the habit enthusiastically as a child and grew up to be as tall, clear-eyed and sane as the next emu.'

46. I also enjoyed considerable Job satisfaction, thanks to a particularly lissome youth of that name.

47. Being one to boast – see my incredibly fascinating Footnote 44 opposite, probably the most riveting footnote ever written – I'd just like to point out how poetic that paragraph is; indisputably the most poetic piece of prose ever penned. I'd further like to point out the pleasing alliteration of the phrase 'the most poetic piece of prose ever penned'.

   A Poet adds: 'Bollocks!'

but they battled in vain, there were so few of them and so many of us.

It couldn't last, of course. Eventually He sobered up, took a befuddled look at what was happening and decided to act. The action He took was absolutely typical. Suffering from the biggest and worst hangover in history, He went right over the top. His dipsomanic philosophy being, if you can't beat 'em, wipe 'em out.

CLAP!
FLASH!
PUFF!

A flood raced across the face of the Earth, total inundation, mass drownings – which rushed us off our feet down here – and only Noah and his holier-than-everyone family preserved.

So we started all over again. The first few generations of Noah's descendants were as goody-goody as he, but they soon got bored with living lives untainted by indulgence and, after a little first-rate tempting, they were taking to sin like Adam did to cleaving.

If anything they exceeded even Adam, especially the denizens of Sodom and Gomorrah who were probably my most enthusiastic converts and aptest pupils. Not only did the Sodomites and Gomorrans commit each and every one of Seven so-called Deadly Sins on a regular daily basis, they even invented an Eighth.[48]

Unfortunately, the fun to be had in Sodom and Gomorrah was short-lived. In an inexcusable burst of alcoholic ill-

48. In addition to Pride, Anger, Envy, Lust, Gluttony, Greed and Sloth, the
    Sodomites and Gomorrans occasionally committed the heinous sin of
    Globbery, a practice so vile and disgusting that it even repulsed the
    people who performed it. Personally, I only tried it once and found it
    mildly pleasurable, considerably more pleasurable than my partner who,
    as a result, was struck both dumb and doubly incontinent and was never
    able to play the zither again. I was never able to indulge in Globbery
    after that because by the time the sores had healed and the swelling on
    my pancreas had subsided, the world's entire supply of unicorns –
    without which any small thrill received from Globbery was impossible –
    had been wiped out in the holocaust that struck the twin cities.

130

temper The Old Moaner obliterated them from the Earth, saving only Lot, a miserable curmudgeon whose idea of having a good time was to write to *The Sodom Times* suggesting that his fellow citizens had their sexual organs either cut off or sewn up. And, in the case of some of my more enthusiastic and less discriminating acolytes, both.

Still, I got my revenge on Lot by creeping up behind his wife as they were fleeing the city, tapping her on the shoulder and whispering, 'Bet you've never seen one as big as this before!'. Naturally, she couldn't overcome her curiosity and turned to take a surreptitious peek.[49]

For this minor misdemeanour Himself instantly turned her into a pillar of salt, which I later carved into the shape of an immense phallus as a monument to those fun-loving folk who gave the world some of its most pleasurable sexual practices. This thrusting edifice became the Ninth Wonder of The World to which millions flocked, gazing in awe at its towering rigidity and gasping, 'Verily, this is an amazing erection! It makes The Colossus of Rhodes look like he's suffering from brewer's droop!'[50]

It was typical of His over-reaction to raze entire cities to the ground just because the people living in them knew how to enjoy themselves and, indeed, each other. When I think of all the things I've been blamed for, they pale into insignificance against what He's done in a fit of pique. How many towns have I ever obliterated? Well, admittedly there were one or two minor metropoli but they were just mistakes. That unfortunate business at Pompeii, for example. A simple error that anyone could make. There I was one day, patronizing one of its many excellent whorehouses, spreading a few of the more

49. Let this be a lesson to the sanctimonious among you. It is very unwise to say, 'Get thee behind me, Satan!'. Especially when I'm feeling randy. Which is all the time.

50. It has always been believed that there were only Seven Wonders of the Ancient World. The Author claims that the Phallus of Sodom was the Ninth and that the Eighth was the Hanging Baskets of Nineveh which although less impressive in sheer size than The Hanging Gardens of Babylon were generally agreed by experts to contain far prettier trailing lobelia. (In the publishers' opinion, this whole story should be taken with a pillar of salt.)

virulent venereal diseases, when I eavesdropped a customer asking his harlot, 'Did the earth move for you?'. Hearing her say it didn't, I thought I'd help out. Trouble is, I sometimes forget my own power. Pity about Pompeii, it was shaping up to be my kind of town.

So was San Francisco, until the earthquake in 1906. Of course, it's been blamed on the San Andreas Fault. Rubbish! The fault was entirely mine. I only meant to hit it with a minor tremor, just to shake things up a bit and cause some amusing panic and confusion. Instead, I somewhat overdid it. Oh, well, not to worry. It was soon rebuilt and is back in business as a pleasure centre. At least temporarily.[51]

However, I will not take the blame for every disaster that strikes the Earth. I had nothing whatsoever to do with The Black Death. Plagues have never been among my favoured catastrophes, there's no fun and little profit in them. To find the culprit, look Upstairs. Plagues are His speciality – locusts, frogs, boils, He's supplied them all.

And look what He did to the first-born of Egypt – slew the lot of them! Such profligate waste! He may be omnipotent but He lacks style. And He's short-sighted – an astute business-man, like myself, doesn't massacre a generation. What you need is some forward planning – I'd have spared the grubby little brats so that later I could lead them astray and they'd mature into first-rate trouble-makers.

Such subtleties are completely lost on Him. He sticks to His old-fashioned ways – chastizing and smiting, purging and decimating, summoning up plagues and pestilences with a click of His fingers, laying waste to perfectly good tracts of real estate with fire, flood and thunderbolt.

All that carnage and slaughter, and the extraordinary thing is that He's got away with it for five thousand years!

51. That's got you San Franciscans worried, hasn't it? Just teasing! You're safe for a while. I won't tell you exactly how long but if any of you are planning to read *War and Peace*, get started on it as soon as you've finished this book. Incidentally, to those of you living in nearby Los Angeles, who may also be worried about the imminence of an earth-quake, I just say this – I hope you're enjoying my book, and although it is drawing towards its brilliant conclusion, have you ever thought of taking a speed-reading course?

Not only that but people worship Him for it! It's enough to drive me to Tee-Totalism.

Don't the fools who venerate Him realize that He's past it? Ga-ga! Far too senile for the job. It's time He made way for a younger Supreme Being, someone with drive, energy, ideas, marketing skills, the ability to read the bottom line and do some astute number-crunching, soul-wise.

Just imagine what things would be like if I was in charge!

Chapter Twenty-Four
Let Pandemonium Reign!

 f I ruled the world, *when* I rule the world, the first thing I will do is issue My One Commandment.
THOU SHALT DO WHAT THE HELL YOU LIKE!

After that anything goes!

And the first to go will be Christmas, Easter and every other festival associated with the usurped pretender and his son. Then we will defrock all his priests and strip his nuns, parading them naked through the thronging streets to be tormented and abused by My howling, blood-crazed mobs.

Heretics who refuse to recant their errant beliefs and abase themselves before My majesty will be subjected to lingering deaths of unimaginable agony at the hands of My followers. And the hounds of Hell will feast upon their flesh.

Then the revels will commence! Lust and greed, anger and gluttony will be unleashed as the world cavorts to the frenzied tattoo of My demonic drumbeat!

All will be chaos and pandemonium, over which I, The Lord

of Misrule, will preside as each of you prances and capers to do My diabolic bidding.

Join Me and all this will come to pass. Together we will create Hell on earth!

And Mine will be the kingdom and the power and the glory!

For ever and ev...

CLAP!

*

FLASH!

*

PUFF!

Croak!

Due to circumstances beyond his control, the author has unexpectedly been forced to abandon this manuscript.
Any reader wishing to contact the author may address correspondence to:

MURIEL TOAD, ESQ.,
THE THIRD LILYPAD FROM THE LEFT,
THE DUCK POND,
EREWHON,
THE SPACE – TIME CONTINUUM.

AMEN!

PS. In My trade we call this a 'Deus ex machina'. All it took was one click of My fingers. Not bad for a senile, alcoholic dwarf in a ginger toupée.

SINDEX

Figures in *italic* denote illustrations.
Figures in **bold** denote principal entries.
Figures in ***bold italic*** denote that the printer is confused.

AARDVARK, as a sexual aid, see Bestiality

ABOVE, see Below

ANGER 3, 7, *13*, 48. See also Ire

ANIMAL THAT LOOKS LIKE A HEARTH RUG AND HANGS UPSIDE DOWN FROM TREES, see Sloth

ART, EROTIC, see illustrations pp. *55–64*

ART, ERRATIC, see work of Jackson Pollack

AURAL SEX, see Zones, Erroneous

AVARICE, see Rice, Ava

BELOW, see Above

BESTIALITY, having sex with George, Angie, Edna and other members of the Best family including Fluff the Aardvark; 99, 102, *121*

BORGE, Lucrezia, *57*

BORGIA, Victor, *88*

CATAMITE, 64; Dogamite, 65; Marmite, 66

CONDOMS, see Letters, French

DEADLY SINS, 7. See also Seven Deadly Sins

DRUGS, hard, 45; soft, 47; wobbly, 49

ELSEWHERE, see Seven Dwarfs

ENVY, 4; Jealousy, 12. (Jealousy won in extra time.) See also Monster, Green-eyed

GENITALIA, FEMALE, see Maidenhead

GENITALIA, MALE, see inside trousers

GOMORRAH, The Sin of, see Sink Tidies

GLOBBERY, 22; its influence on the Metaphysical Poets, 0

GLUTTONY, see Greed

GREED, 1, 4, 9, 10, *11*, 14, 19, 20, 21, 22, *23*, 24, 26, 28, 30–38, *40*, 44, 45, 47, 50–62, 64, 66, 73, 77, 80, *83–85*, 90, 91, 93, 95, 96, 97, 98, 99, 100, 103–106, *108*, 111, 115, 118, 120, 124, 125, 127, 129–131, *132*, 140, 144, 151 and as many other pages as possible.

INDECENCY, 1; Indecency, Gross, 144

INSECT, sexual relations with member of one's own family, 45; possibility that it's a misprint of 'incest', 97

IRE PURCHASE, buying anger on,

LETTERS, FRENCH – é and ç – 27; see also Letters, Greek

LETTERS, GREEK – αβΩδ – the rudest word in the world, 77; see also W********k, the rudest word in the universe.

LINGUS, Cunni, *69*; see also Lingus, Aer

LUST, 1–298, passim

MAIDENHEAD, town on River Thames near Windsor, Berkshire, England; population (1981) 49,038. Not to be confused with female genitalia, and seldom is, 34

MASTURBATION, harmful effects of, see Myopia

MONSTER, GREEN-EYED, 86; blue-eyed, 88; one-eyed, 89

MYOPIA, see an optician, but with difficulty

NERO, and the dangers of barbecues, 139

139

ONAN the Barber, 52. Not to be confused with Conan The Barbarian, 28

ORAL CONTRACEPTION, see 'No!'

ORAL SEX, see Telephone Calls, Dirty. Not to be confused with Aural Sex, see Zones, Erroneous.

PENIS, see Sword

PRIDE, coming before fall, 6; fall coming before winter, 7

RASPUTIN, madness of, 36; sexual perversions of, 37; mass murders of, 38; petit-point embroidery of, *39*

RICE, AVA, the Wickedest Woman In The World, 38–26–34.

RIPPER, JACK THE, true identity of, see Victoria, Queen

SAW, see See

SEE, see Saw

SEESAW, Daw, Marjorie, and use of for sexual stimulation, 99

SEVEN DEADLY SINS, 7, 77, 777

SEVEN NOT ACTUALLY DEADLY BUT HIGHLY CONTAGIOUS SINS, 8

SEVEN OTHER SINS THAT CAN MAKE YOU FEEL VERY UNWELL, 78

SEVEN DWARFS, unusual sexual relationship with Snow White, see elsewhere

SIN, Wages of, 3, 15, 22 and £400 per week.

SINK TIDIES, extraction from bodily orifices of, 12

SLOTH, mentioned on many pages but it's far too much effort to list them all

SCREWOM, city near Sodom, 76

SODOFF, Russian city, 374

SODOM, parks, gardens and municipal art gallery, 18; stews, brothels, dives, bars, massage parlours, gaming-houses, opium dens and bordellos, 3–336 inc.

SOIXANTE-NEUF, 69

STONES, see Styx

STYX and Stones, uses for when breaking bones, 96

SWORD, the pen is mightier than, 88

TRANSVESTICISM see T.V. which frequently shows men dressed as women

VICES, wide variety of, 73. Also complete range of hammers, screwdrivers, bradawls and other ironmongery, 74. Catalogue supplied on request

VLAD THE IMPALER, *73*

VLAD THE IMPALA, *37*

WHORE OF BABYLON, The, 15, 27, 96, 297–55478 (0295, if you're calling from outside Babylon)

WARLOCKS, a kick in the, 64

W********K, the rudest word in the history of the universe, 1*4

ZONES, ERROGENOUS, *19*, 55, 298

ZONES ERRONEOUS, including Aural Sex, Adam's mistaken use of Eve's ear, 12

ZYTHUM, word describing type of beer made by the Ancient Egyptians and not often found in books like this, 1, 6, 9, 15, 17, *22*, 38, 46, 59, 64, 77, 82, 93, 186

ZZOGOTHANTHA, and her enormous bust, *4*; other large statues of, *5*

RECOMMENDED READING

In the light of what has befallen The Author, the publishers would strongly recommend the reader to 'The Bible', both Old and New Testaments.

ALSO RECOMMENDED

The Book of Common Prayer
Hymns Ancient and Modern

NOT RECOMMENDED

Other works by The Author, especially:
'Teach Yourself Alkemy'
'Teach Yourself Neckromancy'
'Teach Yourself Sorsery'
'Teach Yourself Speling'

ERRATA

The Publishers apologize for the many errors of fact that riddle this work.

We would most particularly like to apologize for the most grievous mistake of all – ever having published it.

The Managing Director would like to apologize and take full responsibility. He particularly regrets that being, as he now is, a small brown stain, the result of a well-directed thunderbolt, he is unable to do this personally.

THE F!END

(handwritten correction showing "FI" inserted above, with caret below between "THE" and "END")

TO BE
CONTINUED

God

The Ultimate Autobiography

Pan Books
London, Sydney and Auckland

God

The Ultimate Autobiography

First published 1988 by Ebury Press

This edition published 1989 by Pan Books Ltd
Cavaye Place, London SW10 9PG

9 8 7 6 5 4 3 2 1

© Jeremy Pascall 1988

© Illustrations: Martin Brown 1988

ISBN 0 330 30973 0

Printed and bound in Great Britain by
Richard Clay Ltd, Bungay, Suffolk.

DEDICATION

This book is dedicated to Noah.
Who begat Ham, Shem and Japhet.
And Japhet begat Magog, Madai, Javan, Tubal,
Meshech, Tiras and Gomer.
And Gomer begat Ashkenaz, Riphath and Togarmah.
And Togarmah begat Seba, Havilah, Sabtah,
Raamah, Sabtecah and Kevin.
And Kevin begat Wayne, Shane, Duane and Rover.
And Rover begat Alan, Merrill, Jay, Donny and
Little Jimmy.
And Little Jimmy begat Michael, Jermaine, Jackie,
Marlon and Tito.
And Tito begat Groucho, Chico, Harpo, Zeppo,
Gummo and Omo.
And Omo begat Brillo, Brasso, Glitto and Liquid
Gumption.
And Gumption begat John, John, John, John, John,
John and Kenneth, also known as John.
And Kenneth, also known as John, begat John-John.
And John-John begat John-Paul.
And John-Paul 1 begat John-Paul 2, George-Paul
and Ringo-Paul.
And Ringo-Paul begat Gordon, George, Jackie,
Bobby, Bobby, Alan, Geoff, Roger, Martin and Nobby.
And Nobby begat Sidney.
And Sidney didn't begat anybody because he had a
very close friend called Big Gordon.
But Big Gordon begat Huey, Dewey and Louey.
And Louey begat Andrew, Lloyd and Webber.
And Webber begat 'Jesus Christ Superstar' and never
paid Me any royalties.

Introduction

should have thought this is the one autobiography that needs no introduction. After all, everyone knows who I am. In all due modesty – and I'm nothing if not modest, which is not easy when you're the Supreme Being – I must be the most famous person in the entire fifteen universes.[1]

Is there anyone who hasn't heard of Me in one of My many forms? With My colossal following this book is bound to be the greatest thing since sliced manna and yet the publishers – oh, they of little faith! – felt some words of introduction were necessary and implied that

1. This is the first indication we have had that there is more than one Universe. Either this is a divine revelation or The Author is prone to exaggeration, a trait frequently found in the extremely aged.

if I didn't supply them they'd ask someone else to write a foreword.

The name mentioned was Terry Wogan, who is apparently the second most famous person after Me. I, of course, objected. If anyone is going to do it, it has to be God and not someone who thinks he is Me.

I've encountered this sort of thing before; a film was made about Me – *Oh, God!* – and without any consultation they cast someone called George Burns as Me. I do object to being played by an actor who is actually older than I am. Or, at least, *looks* older. I was so annoyed I nearly phoned Interfauna to order them to send down a plague of locusts.

So, rather than have someone speak on My behalf I have graciously consented to write this brief introduction with the help of My holy ghost writer.

Do you know the most asked question in history? Of course you don't because you're not omniscient and I am. All-knowing, all-seeing, that's Me. Keep that in mind if you're thinking of stealing this book.

The most asked question in history is this: Does God exist? And my answer? Do I exist? Is the Pope Catholic? Well, as it turns out, he is. Which is a shock because he was supposed to be Jewish. A massive cock-up while I wasn't watching. But I can't be everywhere, can I? All right, I *can* but it's very tiring when you get to My age. Which you won't.

I most certainly *do* exist. Who else do you think created the Earth and every thing that's on it? Martians? Even assuming they did, who do you think created Martians? And who do you think wiped them out after they got too big for their boats?[2]

It is precisely because I do exist that in My infinite wisdom (and please note I am the only person who can

truly claim His wisdom is infinite), I have decided to write this book.

You will be aware that the last book about Me is the biggest-seller in the history of the world. It would have been the biggest in the history of the fifteen universes but there are many things you don't know, including the fact that in a galaxy as yet undiscovered by Homo Sapiens another of my books – *God on Gardening* – has outsold even The Bible.[3]

I felt it was time The Bible was put into its proper context. It's a good book, in fact it's *The* Good Book, but it was only a biography, and an *unauthorized* one at that. I didn't even write it. In fact, God knows how many people did and even I've forgotten. With such a large team of authors, inaccuracies are bound to creep in and I will correct them in the course of this, definitive, work.

Furthermore, I'm not sure it depicted Me in My best light. For most of the Old Testament I'm made out to be a bad-tempered geriatric who went around visiting boils and pestilence on all-and-sundry. The fact is I'm a Merciful God, sometimes *too* merciful considering what I've let you get away with. I mean, inventing the barbecue is one thing, but testing it on poor Joan of Arc is quite another.

2. This is not a misprint. The Author reveals that the life-form He created on Mars had exceptionally large feet, so large that they wore small ships on them and thus travelled along the Martian canals. The Author wiped them out in a fit of pique because, He contends, walking on water is reserved only for His son.

3. *God on Gardening* is not currently available. It is hoped that this work and its companion volume – *God Housekeeping – How To Have a Heavenly Home* – will be published in the near future.

JOAN OF ARC

BURNT AT THE STEAK (WELL DONE)

And, let's face it, parts of The Bible are terribly boring – all that dreary business of who begat whom, it reads like the Israelite telephone directory – and there's hardly a joke in it. What most people don't realize is that I have a highly developed sense of humour. Why else do you think I created the Belgians?

Taking all this into consideration, I decided it was time I wrote My version of the facts, just to put the record straight, correct the many errors and cover some omissions, not least the matter of The Eleven Commandments which I will come to in due course.

In the meantime, one word for any atheists among you: wrong.

THE AUTHOR OF ALL CREATION

In The
Beginning ...

n most autobiographies the subject starts at the beginning, but in My case that's tricky. I have no beginning. And, for that matter, I have no end. I'm Infinite. So it makes starting the story difficult. Not to mention ending it. In theory this book could continue indefinitely, which, of course, raises practical difficulties like the immense size of it and the fact that no one would live to read it all the way through. Except Me and that narrows its commercial appeal.[4]

4. It was only with the greatest difficulty that we dissuaded The Author from His original intention of having the entire book inscribed on tablets of stone. While agreeing that this would be a considerable deterrent to shoplifters, we had to point out it would also discourage potential purchasers. He relented when He recalled the damage caused by the two tablets He handed down to Moses, causing the prophet to wear a surgical truss for the rest of his life.

To start as near to the beginning as I can, I wasn't actually born. I just *was*. I still am. I always have been and I always will be. Being Immortal is very nice in most respects – I don't have to worry about things like bus passes and pension schemes – but being Infinite has its drawbacks. For example, time has no meaning; I can be idly day-dreaming and suddenly realize that most of recorded history has passed without My even noticing. Suddenly I have to zoom back through the centuries to where I am supposed to be. As a result I always seem to be running about two hundred years behind schedule and this unpunctuality makes life – or, to be precise, after-life – difficult for members of My staff who never know when I'm going to turn up for a meeting. But, as I always say, What's a millennium between friends? And they always laugh. When you're God you find your little jokes go down rather well.

The other drawback to being Infinite is that I have so much to remember. Most people have trouble remembering what they did yesterday, but not only do I have to remember what happened yesterday, I've also got to remember what's going to happen tomorrow. For example, is the world due to end? And if so, which world? There are, after all, 7,946,587,632 of them. That was at the last count. By the time you read this there may be a few more. Or perhaps several less. And one of them might be your Earth. (That's one of My little jokes, and very funny too. If the destruction of your Earth really was imminent I'd hardly be publishing this, would I? The ways in which I move, My wonders to perform, may be mysterious but they're not bloody stupid.)

So, now, perhaps you can appreciate some of the problems of being Infinite and how it makes starting a

book difficult. However, I know that you'd like Me to start the story where it concerns you. Or, rather, your microscopic little planet which, though I say it Myself, is one of My better creations. I particularly like the colour scheme, all those greens and blues. Very restful, don't you think? So much nicer than the orange and cerise I used for Dandropy (thirty-ninth galaxy of the fourth universe – turn left after Nibolt and ask again).

I suppose you're surprised that I didn't create your planet first, typical of human egotism. But if it helps, yours was the first planet I created in your galaxy of your universe.

If you've read your Bible carefully – which you haven't, have you? – how many of The Eleven Commandments can you recite? Exactly! You're stuck after "Thou Shalt Not Commit Adultery", aren't you?

All right, even if you've only skimmed The Bible, looking for the rude bits like The Whore of Babylon, you'll know that it starts with Genesis.[5]

The first words of Genesis are: "In the beginning God created the heaven and the earth."

This is true in so far as it goes. Certainly I created Heaven first because I wanted somewhere to live, I can't tell you how boring it used to be just wandering aimlessly through the chartless void, with nobody to talk to, nothing much to do and nowhere to call home. So I decided to create a place to live which would be My idea of ... well ... heaven.

I know you mortals are fascinated by what Heaven is really like, probably because most of you won't see it, unless you repent the error of your ways

5. The Whore of Babylon can be found in Revelations xvii-xix, but you're going to be disappointed.

and pretty damn quick. To satisfy your idle curiosity I'll tell you that it has the best of everything – delicious food, magnificent wine, a superb climate and beautiful vistas on every side. A bit like France. But without the French. Not that I'm prejudiced – some of My best saints are French.

So I created this little place. Nothing too ostentatious – just somewhere to hang My halo, as it were. Although don't take this halo business too literally, I obviously don't wear it all the time. It might look good in portraits but, take it from Me, having a light blazing over your head gives you a frightful migraine. Not to mention its effect on others. Look what it did to Saul on the road to Damascus – blinded the poor chap. My fault entirely, I should have dipped My headlight.

Mind you, a halo has its practical uses when one is venturing into the dark abyss of measureless Space to do odd jobs. It does leave both hands free to get on with the work and came in very useful when I decided to create your Earth.

That project came about because, frankly, I was bored. When you have limitless powers you want to try them out, see what you can do with them, maybe create the odd solar system here and there. And then, if the whim takes you, use the stars for juggling practice. Although the fun went out of juggling when I dropped a particularly large asteroid on My toe. It wasn't until then I realized I suffered from bunions. In fact, it wasn't until then that I realized I'd created bunions. Still can't imagine why I did.

Anyway, out of boredom I'd knocked up a few planets scattered through the universes but the results hadn't been altogether satisfactory.

Looking through My scrap-book I see that

Prototype XI was an interesting experiment. It looked absolutely marvellous with its seventeen oceans, the problem was its shape. Being square the oceans kept slopping over the sides and dripping through Space until they rained on to Prototype VII. This in itself would not have been a disaster if it wasn't for the extremely low temperatures of Outer Space. Sadly, Prototype VII was destroyed when it was hit by a hailstone three times its own size.

Then there's Prototype XIII. I think I must have been going through My Henry Moore period. Not a great success. Still, nothing's wasted, it proved to be a useful model for Gruyère cheese.[6]

There were other experiments: Prototype XXI was My first attempt at creating a planet with its own life-form. Never having made a life-form before I didn't know what to use as My model. You probably know that Man was created in My own image. But I am ever-changing, I can adopt whatsoever form I like – worth remembering the next time you feel like crushing an ant; it can come as a nasty surprise when an insect turns you into a pillar of salt.

The week in which I created Adam and Eve I just happened to be in the form of a bipedal anthropoid and used that as My template. Rather crude, admittedly, and not particularly beautiful but good enough for you. However, when I was fashioning the creatures on Pro-totype XXI I had assumed a completely different form. And, frankly, although lawnmowers are pleasing in

6. The Author insists on adding: "Do you know why Gruyère is My favourite cheese? Because it's holey!" The collaborator is delighted to include this extremely amusing joke. Not least because The Author jocularly threatened to turn him into a "*holey* ghost writer" if it was edited out.

their way, they aren't particularly successful as humanoids and an absolute disaster when it comes to procreation.

But I see you're getting restless and want Me to describe the creation of your own piffling little Earth. That's the trouble with you anthropoids, you're so impatient; if you took things a little slower and thought a bit longer you could have avoided so much unpleasantness. Sometimes I wonder why I bother with creatures who consider the peak of their civilization to be the bedside radio alarm clock with snooze button facility.

Be that as it may, having practiced on other planets, I thought I had ironed out most of the problems when I finally turned My attention to Earth . . .

Monday And Tuesday ... And Earth was Created

created the Earth and all that's upon it in six days. No, that's not quite accurate; for most of the first twenty-four hours I was working in the dark – except for the glow from My halo – because I hadn't yet invented the day. Well, it stands to reason, doesn't it? To have day you've got to have daylight. And to have daylight you've got to have a sun.

So first I had to create the sun. I said: "Let there be light!" And there was light! Eventually. It took a while. As even you may know, the sun is a ball of burning gas. And you know how difficult it can be to light the gas at the best of times. Imagine what it's like when you haven't yet invented matches, or even fire? So I had to start from scratch and that took a bit longer than I expected and set My plans back, so I put myself on

overtime and created the Earth and all that's on it in six days *and* six nights and damn near knackered Myself doing it.

The Bible makes it all sound so simple. "And God said, 'Let there be firmament'." And, according to The Bible, in a twinkling, there was firmament. Balderdash! For a start, I don't use words like "firmament", I'm a plain-speaking God who believes in calling a spade a spade, and a sky a sky.

What I actually said was: "Let there be thingy." Because I hadn't yet got around to giving the bits of the Earth any names; that came a lot later and it wasn't Me who decided that the bit above your head would be called "sky", it was Adam. I wanted to call it "waxtl" but the bloody fool couldn't get his tongue round it, because he had his mouth stuffed full of apple. But that's another story and we'll come to it later.

After some trial and error – it being Monday and Me never being quite at My best on a Monday morning – I created the waxtl (I still think it's a better name than "sky") and looked through my colour charts to select a blue which was striking without being garish and then dotted it around with some fluffy yellow clouds. Yes, yellow. Complete disaster! Could have got away with it had the yellow been pastel, but being inexperienced I chose a shade that was sudden to the point of stridency. Used it later for canaries. On them it looks good, but on clouds ... hopeless! In the end, I took the line of least resistance and plumped for white.

So that was the sky done and already a whole day had passed. The very first day and not a bad one, all things considered, even though I was slightly behind schedule.

Tuesday morning, I was up with the lark. Or

would have been had I created the lark but birds weren't on My list until Thursday afternoon. According to My diary, the first thing I made on Tuesday morning was breakfast, another first and something of an accident. I was fiddling around with a little model of the planet and thought it looked good enough to eat. So I ate it. Delicious! Inventing breakfast is a splendid way to start the day.

After satisfying the inner God, I turned My attention to the Earth.

If you believe The Bible – and I'm not saying you shouldn't believe it, just don't take it too literally – I merely clicked My fingers and created the Earth. As simple as that!

Again, I'm not saying I can't just click My fingers and an earth will appear – after all, I *am* The Supreme Being – but as we say up here, "The impossible we can do immediately, miracles take a little longer"; rather witty, don't you think? Of course you do. I had it printed on a little wooden plaque and nailed on the wall, next to another saying, "You don't have to be God to work here, but it helps."

Finger-clicking is all very well in theory, but in practice a bit of thought has to go into the ordering of an earth. And especially what you call The Earth. I didn't want to order the wrong model. For example, you wouldn't like to live on a flat Earth, would you? Apparently, some of you seem to think you do, but then some of you might prefer bright yellow clouds – there's no accounting for taste.

After much thought I decided on a round planet, which solved the messy problem of the oceans spilling all over the universe, deterred idiotic flat-earthers from attempting to hurl themselves off the edge to prove

their point and had the added advantage of being easily rolled around your universe. Important that, as I nearly ruptured Myself trying to shift Prototype XXXV from one part of a galaxy to another. For some reason that escapes Me, I'd shaped it like a Chesterfield sofa and had omitted to give it castors. You know, sometimes I wonder whether I'm the right God for the job.

Another reason I made your Earth round is that if it had proved a failure, I could use it for a game of snooker.[7]

Having finally decided on the shape, I looked at the size. I didn't want it to be too big – there's nothing more vulgar than an over-large planet – but at the same time I wanted something roomy enough to take different styles of continents, a long, thin one here, contrasting with a boxy one there. And having made My mind up about that, I was ready to roll up My sleeves and get down to work.

Looking at your Earth now, I don't think I gave it enough time. Frankly, it was a rushed job and mistakes were made. After all, nobody's perfect. No, that's not true; *I* am perfect but even I can find room for improvement, something the Pope would do well to remember. Theologically speaking, he is infallible but what do you make of a pontiff who goes around kissing airport runways and names himself after two of the Beatles? And the wrong two at that. Personally, I always preferred George-Ringo as a name, but would he listen to Me?

7. When questioned, The Author explained that having abandoned juggling with planets, He took up playing snooker with them. Had He not been satisfied with His week's work, the Earth would have been the green, Mars one of the reds and our moon the white. When asked what He used for pockets, He replied, "What do you think is the purpose of those things your astronomers call 'Black Holes'?"

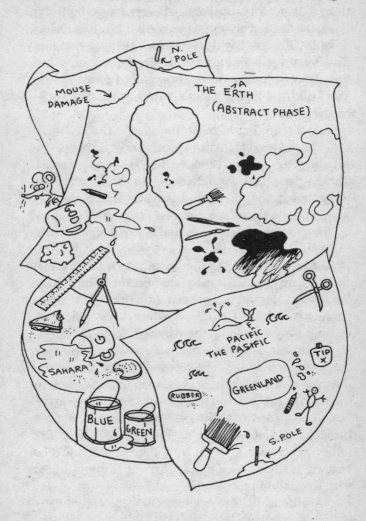

I digress. All-in-all, the Earth turned out pretty well but I realize with hindsight that it leaves something to be desired. The Sahara Desert, for example. It's much too large; a bit of sand is nice but I think I should have been content with the Gobi, neat and compact. The Sahara is definitely O.T.T. But, of course, it was never meant to be a desert; originally I planned it as The Milk-And-Honey Theme Park but I spilled coffee on the blueprints.

And speaking of big – the Pacific Ocean! What could I have been thinking about? I must have been in My Blue Period when I created it and got carried away. There's room there for a decent-sized continent, something along the lines of Australia, but preferably without the Australians. Not that I'm prejudiced but of all the children of Adam I do find Australians the most ... well ... raucous.

If I were designing the Earth today, I'd do something more creative with the Pacific, bung in a landmass somewhere between America and Asia, a chunky island like Greenland, which, upon reflection, is completely wasted up there by the North Pole.

However, I won't hear a word against the Poles, the way they balance the top and the bottom of the Earth is symmetrically perfect. Granted, they are on the biggish side but you must allow the creative artist His whims. Just think yourself lucky that I'd worked through My Cubist phase on Prototype XXXVI. Try living on that for a couple of millennia and you'd be begging me for a nice round globe topped and tailed with a couple of pretty Poles.

Aesthetically, I'm not sure I'm completely happy with the Northern Hemisphere. It looks a bit top-heavy. Europe and Asia do tend to sprawl, but America

is marvellous – worth every minute I spent on it; in fact, possibly My finest creation. I just wish I'd been more selective about the people who inhabit it. What I particularly like is the way North America runs into South America and the whole thing stretches from top to bottom with just the narrowest of joins in the middle.

I confess that joining them together was an afterthought. Originally, North and South America were quite separate but as I was fiddling around with the Caribbean, just haphazardly decorating it with a handful of islands, sprinkling them hither and yon as One does, it occurred to Me that one of them would fit perfectly in the gap between Nicaragua and Colombia. And that's how Panama came to be where it is, instead of just off Cuba.

Taking one thing with another, I'm pretty satisfied with the Earth although I'm well aware that some of you are always whingeing that it's too small – so ungrateful; I spent an entire week creating your Earth and all you can do is moan. Don't blame Me if it's overcrowded, that's your own fault. You should exercise more restraint in the matter of procreation. If one child is good enough for Me, it should be more than enough for you.

And if you don't like the planet I created for you, well, let's see you do better. Go on, try making your own. You think you're so smart, but in the two thousand years since I sent My boy down to sort you out, you still haven't managed to design something as simple as a decent corned beef tin ...

Wednesday
to Friday

o Monday and Tuesday were taken up with creating the waxtl and the planet Earth. On Wednesday I brought forth grasses, herbs, trees and various greengroceries. That was a good day, very enjoyable, but exhausting. Well, you know what hard work gardening can be; just imagine how I felt after creating every single plant from lichen to the California redwood, not to mention roses, nasturtiums, seaweed and the Venus flytrap in between. Even I'm amazed by My achievement but I confess that there were disappointments. Cacti, for example; I never really got them right. Can't imagine what I meant them to look like, but certainly they turned out wrong.

Maybe I had the plans upside down. Anyway, too late to worry now.[8]

That brings Me to Thursday. What happened on Thursday? Well, according to The Bible, I created the sun, the moon and the stars, but that can't be right because I distinctly remember doing the sun first thing on Monday morning. And, splendid though the moon may be, I surely didn't spend an entire day making it. When all's said and done and when poets have finished rhapsodizing over its silver luminescence – a most pleasing effect, to be sure – the moon is just an empty lump of rock which I could have knocked out in any idle moment.

Frankly, I've never understood why you anthropoids have spent so much time, energy and money trying to get to your moon, it isn't worth the trip. And you're going to be terribly disappointed when you eventually reach some of the other planets, although Pluto is quite interesting, being the home of the biggest creature I ever created, the Glarriper. An interesting beast with some remarkable mating habits. But, enough! I don't want to spoil the surprise.

I'm sure I didn't spend a whole day creating the moon and, by the same token, the stars couldn't have taken very long. They look like they were thrown together before breakfast, just sprinkled at random through Space. If I had taken any time over them, I'd have arranged them into some more interesting patterns. There's a lot you can do with stars when you put

8. Interestingly, cacti are omitted from The Author's book, *God on Gardening*. However, He does include an entry on Accountants, which He seems to think are some form of vegetable. Whether this is a mental aberration due to age is unclear.

your mind to it. I recall another galaxy in which I arranged them so that if you draw imaginary lines between them they spell out a message. I wish I'd done the same for you, so that every time you gazed up at the night waxtl you'd see:

"God Says: The Meek Shall Inherit The Earth, So Don't Let Estate Agents Con You Out Of It."

No, if My memory serves Me correct, and of course it does, I only spent a couple of hours on Thursday bunging bits of rock around the waxtl. The rest of that day and all of Friday were devoted to making animals.

Thursday and Friday were two of the most interesting days of My whole infinite existence. I like animals – in many ways I prefer them to humans. They don't get ideas above their station, they don't complain and they don't talk back.

I never hear rhinoceroses moaning on at Me about the way they look. Your average rhino is quite happy with the way I created him; he doesn't think it odd to have a horn sticking out of his nose. Mind you, he doesn't realize that it was left over from the prototype of a cockroach eight foot high. No, rhinos don't complain, mostly, I suppose, because your average rhino doesn't have much in the way of a brain.[9]

9. It seems The Author designed several beasts that never got off the drawing board. The Giant Cockroach is but one example. There was also a large carnivorous gerbil and a type of warthog which was so outstandingly ugly that even warthogs of the opposite sex would have refused to mate with it, causing it to become extinct within one generation. Additionally, He intended a species of boneless fish. Despite its obvious advantages of being much easier to eat without the risk of choking and saving considerable time in restaurants while waiters make a mess of filleting, The Author never managed to solve the inherent structural problem of an animal that was so floppy it couldn't swim or breathe.

Admittedly, the rhino has more brain than, say, an Afghan hound. Of all My myriad and wondrous creations the Afghan is probably the most stupid (with the obvious exception of the guinea pig. And politicians, but I can't be blamed for them. Entirely the fault of evolution. Or lack of it.) Simple reason, really; I fashioned the Afghan for speed and beauty. Aerodynamically speaking, it is a triumph – just look at that wedge-shaped head, almost no wind-resistance at all. But the trouble is, it's so compact that I left very little room for any cranial matter; consequently the Afghan hound has a tiny brain producing a minuscule I.Q. which is barely matched by that of the people who own it.

Of all My works the brain must be My highest achievement. Only I – and I speak with as much modesty as an omnipotent being can muster – only I, could have conceived of it. But it is so complex that even I encountered problems. For example, early brains weren't altogether reliable. To be brutally frank, some were a complete disaster.

Take the dinosaurs – magnificent beasts in most respects but seriously under-powered in the head department. I underestimated the damage that several tons of flesh and muscle could wreak on a virgin planet when guided by a brain that even the dimmest worm would have found wanting.

Hence the downfall of the dinosaurs. First they started eating all the greengroceries I had provided – even the cacti, which gives some measure of exactly how dense they were – and when they'd denuded the place of comestible vegetation, they started eating each other. And when they ran out of other dinosaurs, they ate themselves. There were few more fearsome sights

than to witness a Tyrannosaurus Rex eating its own tail and hind legs and gnawing halfway through its stomach before its brain finally realized it was eating the very thing it was supposed to be filling.

I notice that current scientific thought suggests that the dinosaurs became extinct through evolution, but the fact is the silly brutes destroyed themselves through devolution and actually disappeared up their own alimentary tracts. Never thought of that, did you, Darwin? There's still a lot you jumped-up anthropoid apes can learn.[10]

I created all the fishes of the sea and the beasts of the field, including the creeping and crawling things – in fact, everything from the aardvark to the zorro – during most of Thursday and all of Friday. And yet people still don't believe I did it. People still ask, "Did God really create every living creature, including the creeping and crawling things, in a couple of working days?" Did I? Do birds fly? Well, yes they do, which explains why it took Me so long.[11]

Originally I intended pigs to fly. There was nothing intrinsically difficult in this, at least not for Me, it was just a question of making the wings big and powerful enough. In fact, I had several flocks of them fluttering quite successfully, after I'd nudged them out

10. When asked about evolution, The Author said it was a mistake and that Charles Darwin should have been a stick insect. A slightly enigmatic answer, possibly one of The Author's celebrated jokes. However, He did add: "Given the choice, would you prefer to think you are descended from Me or an orang-utang? But before you answer, consider this: how do you know that I'm not an orang-utang?"

11. The zorro is a South American fox-like wild dog. One can't help feeling The Author is showing off His knowledge.

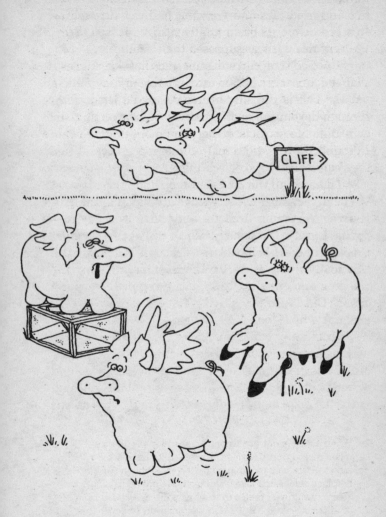

of the trees, but I hadn't realized that the poor creatures suffer terribly from vertigo. No head for heights; they'd get a nose-bleed just by wearing thick socks, and so, in My infinite mercy, I excused them from flying duties and instead strapped wings on some dull little animals I'd made earlier. Birds turned out rather well, all things considered. Unfortunately, as I'd left it rather late in the day, I couldn't get round to converting all of them to flight and so the ostrich never got off the ground. Just as well, really. Imagine a flock of them flying overhead and defecating on everything beneath. You'd be up to your knees in the stuff.

By Friday night I was ready for My bed. After saying My prayers and thanking Myself for My many gifts, I gratefully put My head on My pillow and prepared for another day. And I needed My sleep because Saturday was going to be The Big One.

Saturday ...
Adam

Saturday morning I *was* up with the lark, having finally got around to creating it, and had cause to regret that I didn't design some form of volume control into it.

Having washed and dressed in My overalls – contrary to what you see depicted on the Sistine Chapel ceiling, I don't always wear a white robe, making worlds is a mucky business – I set out to survey all I had created and saw that it was good. In fact, it was bloody marvellous and the very best bit of all was Eden. A little piece of Heaven on Earth.

How can I describe Eden so that you, with your limited intellect, will be able to grasp its beauty? It was, if you like, the first ever Garden Centre. It had everything the discerning God could ask and lacked several things that you seem to appreciate in gardens,

like plaster gnomes, plastic tables with Martini umbrellas, dinky bird baths and carousel washing lines.

The only desirable thing Eden didn't have was staff. Extraordinary, isn't it, but several millennia later you still can't find staff in Garden Centres, and if you do find someone to point you towards the hollyhocks, they've probably only started work that morning and don't know a Sweet William from a pansy. Human evolution isn't all it's cracked up to be.

So there was Eden, measureless acres of perfection, without anyone to till the earth, trim the verges or dead-head the chrysanths. I needed a jobbing gardener and, as they don't grow on trees – although I sometimes wish I'd thought of that method of propagating humans, it would have saved a lot of messy begatting – I had to create someone to take care of the place.

Not just any animal but one which could walk erect and reach up to prune low branches, which had hands dexterous enough to tie back the sweet peas and was strong enough to cart manure across the lawns. In addition, this creature should have enough intellectual capacity to understand and follow simple orders. In short, I needed a modified chimpanzee. (No disrespect to the chimp, which is far too sophisticated to spend its life carting manure around and trying to erect carousel washing lines.)

So I picked up a handful of dust, moulded it in My hands and made Adam, Yes, it *was* as simple as that. The work of but seconds, using whatever materials were lying around. Surprised? You shouldn't be because, when all's said and done, I was only making someone who could do odd jobs around the garden.

Look at it this way, I'd already put most of My energies into creating the really *important* animals,

EDEN
GARDEN
CENTRE

the ones which I'd intended would rule My new planet. Or The Earth, as you call it. Typical human egotism; you call it "Earth" after the stuff beneath your feet but the planet is hardly composed of earth at all. The vast majority of it is ocean and so obviously I'd spent the majority of My time working on the animals that would live in that environment.

Consequently, I'd invented the most intelligent creature in the entire fifteen universes – the dolphin. However, dolphins are so intelligent they quickly realized that running the planet would lead to such evils as tension, stress, ulcers, war and polyester leisure suits and refused to waste their intellect on such trivia.

Instead they sensibly settled for a quiet life of swimming, begatting, eating, begatting, playing, begatting, and performing tricks that seem to entertain the simple-minded descendants of a handyman.

So that's how it happened, I created the first man almost before you could say "Jack Robinson". Not that you would have said "Jack Robinson", because there wasn't anybody of that name around. There was only this over-sized chimp.

I called him Adam, which is a nice enough name – short, easy to remember and rather classier than Sheldon, Darren or Wayne. I did dicker with calling him Geoffrey but it doesn't have the same ring. I didn't bother with a surname. No point really, this Adam was hardly going to be confused with any other. Anyway, I'm not sure I approve of all these names, I've only got one and what's good enough for Me should be quite good enough for you. But, to be fair, there is only one of Me, whereas there are far too many of you. Adam's fault, of course, but we'll come to that later.

Having formed Adam from dust, I breathed life into him by blowing into his nose, which wasn't entirely pleasureable as nostrils are far from being the most exquisite part of the human anatomy. He moaned softly, sneezed violently, stirred into consciousness and scratched his groin.

Within seconds of coming to life, Adam, the first man, rose unsteadily to his feet. He blinked, looked around at the perfection that was Eden, then raised his eyes to the heavens and gazed at the shining glory of his Maker. Then the first man uttered the first words ever heard on Earth. He said: "Well, I'll be buggered!"

It was then I wondered whether I hadn't made a terrible mistake. But you know how it is with hired help, you take what you can get and as he was all I had, I set him to work.

It being his first day I started him off on something simple, fruit-picking. I showed him the trees and the fruit hanging from them and in words of one syllable explained what was expected.

Adam listened and nodded and after a lot of head-scratching he uttered his second sentence. I'll never forget those words which I watched him form with painful slowness. "How much," he asked, haltingly, "does the job pay?"

Then I spake and My voice was as an earthquake, shaking the ground beneath his feet and causing a great wind to howl around him: "I am the Lord Thy God. I created you, fashioned you in My own likeness. You will obey My every command, else I'll turn you back into the dust from whence you came."

Whereupon, hearing these words, he threw himself to the ground, cowering and whimpering before My wrath. He looked so abject and miserable that I took

pity on him and raised him to his feet. "Look," I said, kindly, "this is the deal: you're in My garden and I pay nothing except the wages of sin. But I am a merciful God; if you do as you are told, keep the place tidy and don't take long lunch hours, I'll allow you to have as much fruit as you can eat. Can't say fairer than that, can I?

"You can eat anything in the garden you like but, take My advice, steer clear of those things lying on the ground, which are stones; and, especially, those things over there which look like stones but are, in fact, rabbit droppings.

"Otherwise, everything in Eden is yours for the taking. Except – and I'll say this only once, so listen carefully – *except* the apples from the big tree in the middle of the herbaceous border, just to the right of the snapdragons. Those apples are Mine and Mine alone. Eat one of those and you'll find yourself in big trouble. Understand?"

He nodded mutely.

"Good. Now I've got to go and check whether the Himalayas have set, they were still soft the last time I looked, so you get on with your work. And just remember who's The Boss around here."

And I left him standing there, in the orchard, staring at a pineapple he held in his hand, wondering into which orifice he should insert it.

Later The Same Day . . . Eve

When I created Eve I little realized I was also creating feminism. Now I've nothing against feminists, after all I've had enough experience of being a woman to know exactly how they feel. Yes, let's settle this tedious theological debate once and for all. I *am* a woman . . . when I want to be.

As I keep trying to remind My clergy, I am The Trinity. But they seem to think that being Three-In-One means I'm some sort of lawnmower oil. Let Me make Myself clear: I am God the Father, God the Son and God the Holy Ghost. And I'm more than that; I am also God the Mother, God the Daughter, God the Niece and God the Second Cousin Once Removed. In brief, I am God the Whatever I Want To Be — male, female, animal, vegetable or mineral — so treat your house-

plants, even the cacti, with more respect, because you never know ...

As a woman – when I am a woman – I take great exception to charges of sexism, just because I created Adam before Eve. The explanation is simple. Adam was the prototype, and, frankly, watching him stumbling around Eden, bumping into trees and trying to open a coconut by knocking it vigorously against his forehead, it didn't take Me long to realize that he left plenty of room for improvement.

I decided to have another try. Eve was going to be My masterpiece so I devoted more time to her creation and, of course, I used superior materials. Dust was good enough for Adam but for Eve I worked from living tissues.

As everyone knows, I used one of Adam's ribs. Not, as some think, a spare rib – I was creating life, not testing recipes for a Chinese cookbook.[12]

This was to be My most delicate operation, a pioneering rib transplant. I scrubbed up and prepared to put Adam into a deep sleep – the world's first anaesthetic – but he saved Me the trouble by rendering himself unconscious with his coconut. Then, with utmost care and concentration, I performed the first ribectomy. From that rib came Eve.

And lo! Woman was created.

I gazed upon her and saw she was good. What an improvement! So much better formed, softer, rounder,

12. The Author has, in fact written a companion volume to *God on Gardening* called *Kitchen Miracles*, which includes such recipes as "1001 Things To Do With A Pillar Of Salt"; "Feeding 5000 Unexpected Guests On Loaves And Fishes"; "Water Into Wine" and "How To Convert Devilled Kidneys To Righteousness".

smoother, with none of those ugly dangly bits which had been causing Adam so much trouble and pain as he'd tried to take a short-cut through the brambles.

Gently I re-awoke Adam and presented Eve to him, saying she was to be his partner and they were to live together and share the work equally and told him to take that silly grin off his face while I was talking to him.

Within that one day I had created Adam and Eve, man and woman, and before long they were doing what man and woman would do throughout history. They were arguing.

Arguing about the correct way to open a coconut. Adam still clung to his theory that the best method was to tap it sharply against the forehead, and in consequence invented the headache. Eve suggested using a rock which, eventually, he did, and came close to pioneering the frontal lobotomy. When he recovered consciousness she indicated that next time he should hit the coconut with the rock. But by then it was late on Saturday night, I was exhausted from My labours and, frankly, fed up with humans.

What I needed was a holiday. And so I created Sunday ...

Sunday ...
What I Did On
My Holiday

Having laboured long and hard, I set aside the seventh day as a day of rest. Ever since, people have speculated on how I passed that first Sunday.

As you might expect, I spent much of the day on My knees. Have you any idea how much mess is left after creating a world? It took Me hours of scrubbing before I got My workroom tidy.

As for what I did during the rest of the day – it's none of your damned business. I'm entitled to my private pleasures like anyone else. So keep your nose out of My affairs.

The Second Week

oke up on Monday with a fearful headache.[13] I made My usual ablutions but decided against shaving, partly because My hand was not as steady as I'd have wished and partly because I wanted to see what I looked like in a beard. One of My better decisions; the beard makes Me look more ... well, Godlike ... in portraits. Though I do wish painters would refrain from depicting Me wearing a flowing robe. Makes Me

13. This may indicate that The Author had inadvertently invented the hangover. In fact, the mother and father of hangovers. And neglected to invent Alka-Seltzer. When questioned on the subject The Author was evasive. He merely muttered "chihuahua". Further research reveals that the chihuahua is the only hairless dog; whether this is a result of an early attempt at curing the hangover must remain speculation.

look as though I've forgotten to change out of My nightshirt. Which is nonsense anyway because I've always favoured pyjamas.

Decided to clear My head and have a breath of fresh air by taking a stroll around Eden.

The sun was high in the waxtl. The birds were singing. The trees were in leaf and every plant was blooming, except for the cacti which were stubbornly being prickly.[14]

In the course of My perambulation there was an unfortunate incident; while viewing the cacti and wondering whether it was too late to turn them into something more useful and decorative, like, for example, luxurious reclining garden chairs with detachable, machine-washable chintz covers, I inadvertently trod on the tail of a snake that was basking in their shade. The beast took great exception to this small accident and reacted in what can only be described as a hostile and unforgiving manner. I seem to remember it hissed: "Who do you think you are, God Almighty?" To which I obviously replied, "Yes." Then it said: "In which case, why didn't you give me any legs?" And it slithered away, in high dudgeon muttering darkly to itself and sticking its tongue out in an offensive manner. I sometimes wonder if My small act of carelessness was to have a bearing on subsequent events.[15]

14. The sky was still known as the "waxtl" as Adam had not yet got around to naming his surroundings. There are four possible reasons for this: [a] he hadn't had time; [b] language hadn't been invented; [c] he was too stupid or [d] he was otherwise engaged, as will become apparent.

15. The Author reveals that He now regrets the creation of the snake. He fashioned it before He discovered that He'd used up His remaining stock of legs on the centipede.

I continued My stroll, but of Adam and Eve there was not a sign. Eventually, however, I heard a noise issuing from a clump of blackberry bushes and upon investigating found that within hours of his creation Adam had made two discoveries. The first was begatting and the second was that blackberry bushes are not the ideal places in which to begat.

Obviously I had always intended that humans should begat – Eden was a big garden and would need more hands to tend it, especially if the staff were going to spend their time begatting when they should be spreading the compost – but even I was startled by the rapidity with which Adam (a creature of low intellect who had trouble distinguishing one orifice from another) had found one of the purposes of his ugly dangly bits.

Astonishingly, he was aware of begatting even before the rabbits, both of which, at that point, were too occupied with eating My varied and bounteous green-groceries to turn their minds to other pleasures of the flesh. (Rabbits did not discover begatting for some three weeks when, full to bursting and, perversely, having rejected cacti as a source of food, they explored the possibility of procreation and, like humans, haven't stopped since.)

Although Adam and Eve were the first begatters on Earth, their discovery of the techniques involved came only through trial and error, with Adam doing most of the trying and making most of the errors. But you have to understand this was eons before sex therapists were around to tell him where he was going wrong. And of course, I wasn't inclined to offer any advice as the act of begatting is a matter of indifference to Me. If I feel the need to procreate Myself – which has

49

only occurred once in My infinite existence – I ask the Holy Ghost to see to it on My behalf.[16]

But I digress. I chanced upon Adam and Eve behind this blackberry bush just as he was revealing his great discovery to her. He was, in fact, making excited guttural noises and pointing towards his tumescent nether portions. Eve's reaction was both enthusiastic and swift – she kneed him in the groin. This effectively set back human procreation by several hours and very nearly ended it before it began. In retrospect this may not have been such a bad thing, considering all the problems you humans have caused; if Eve had succeeded in unmanning Adam My creation would have been spared blights like war, torture, nuclear weapons and plastic sink tidies. Sadly, she merely succeeded in cooling Adam's ardour for a short period and forcing his voice up several octaves. An improvement, in My opinion.

Personally, I would like to draw a discreet veil over the development of human begatting, but I am aware it is one of the few topics of interest to most members of your species who have resolutely ignored My Seventh Commandment about not coveting your

16. The question of the Virgin Birth has taxed the finest theological minds – and some bishops of the church – for two millennia. Recent debates about surrogacy have largely ignored the fact that The Author employed not only a surrogate mother but a surrogate father – The Holy Ghost – as well. Atheists have frequently cited the Virgin Mary as an argument against The Author, one recently declaring, "Even if there was a God, would you trust a man who got an unmarried girl pregnant and then tried to blame it on someone else?"

When asked about his view of atheists, The Author replied: "I don't believe in them."

neighbour's ass or, indeed, any other part of his or her anatomy.[17]

I have always thought that the act of begatting is the most ludicrous of human functions. I blame Myself. Had I given it more careful thought I would have designed the entire mechanism differently, probably by eliminating any physical contact. This worked successfully in one of the other universes where I created a single-sex life form that procreated itself by sneezing. This brilliantly simple method worked beautifully for several generations until one great-great-great-grandchild caught a nasty cold, passed it on to its siblings and caused a catastrophic population explosion.

The method I designed for you is much too complicated, appears to be physically uncomfortable (if not, judging from the way some of you do it, downright dangerous) and extremely undignified. I've never understood why it seems to give you so much pleasure. Personally, I prefer a nice cup of tea.

Not that begatting gave Adam much pleasure, at least initially. Having regained his breath, and the lower register of his voice, after his first attempt to introduce Eve to it, he tried again. This time he chose his location more carefully, well away from blackberry bushes, and, after some initial confusion about who was to do what to whom and which organs should go where – a lot of time was wasted as he attempted to whisper seductively into her nose (there were one or two other misapprehensions of a similar nature which I shall not

17. When asked whether Biblical scholars have misinterpreted the Tenth Commandment by implying it means we should not covet our neighbour's donkey, The Author replied: "Donkey? How many people fall in love with donkeys? I thought that sort of thing had died out with Sodom and Gomorrah. Perhaps I didn't use enough brimstone."

elaborate on) – the first human begatting was achieved. This experience left Adam in a state of blissful euphoria and Eve wondering what all the fuss was about.

Nevertheless, they persisted, mostly, I think, because Eve hadn't yet found a grunt that meant "No" and because she was beginning to realize that the first method of contraception was becoming less reliable as Adam became more agile in avoiding the knee in the groin.

Persistence paid off; within a remarkably short time Eve found that begatting was not unpleasant and, indeed, was far more pleasant than the main purpose for which I had put them on Earth – weeding the borders. As I had better things to do than watch the pair of them work through all the possibilities of advanced begatting – including finding three uses for an aubergine that had never occurred to Me when I created it – I left them to it. After all, they couldn't come to much harm while My back was turned.

The Fall of Man

 few days later I was taking a turn round the garden when I became aware that all was not as usual. For a start it was unnaturally quiet. Silence reigned apart from the riffle of the breeze through the leaves, the trilling songs of the birds and the bellow of yet another pain-maddened beast which has tried to browse on the cacti.

It took Me a few moments to realize what was missing – the unmistakable sound of Adam and Eve begatting. No sound at all come from them.

So I called out. But answer came there none. I called again. Still no answer. This was odd. I didn't doubt that they'd heard Me because when I raise My voice it is like unto a great wind that stirs the oceans

and causes the mountains to tremble. This, I find, usually catches people's attention.

I called a third time and when the oceans stopped slopping about and the mountains had come to rest, I heard a small cough behind Me. Turning round I saw Adam. And he saw Me. And then he did a most extraordinary thing, he grabbed a handful of leaves and attempted to cover his nakedness. And as I watched he threw himself to the ground at My feet and howled. And I spake gently unto him, saying, "Adam, why did you cover your nakedness? And, more to the point, why did you use stinging nettles?"

But still Adam howled and so I found him a dock leaf and as he applied it to the affected parts, I said, "Adam, you and I are going to have a little chat, man to God. Tell Me, have you eaten of the fruit of the big tree in the middle of the herbaceous border?"

And Adam nodded.

I am, I think you'll agree, a Merciful God.[18]

However, there are certain things up with which I will not put. In the short time since I had created Adam and Eve I had turned a blind eye on their neglect of the Garden Centre while they were engaged in their begatting experiments. I had overlooked the weeds in the paths, the untrimmed lawns, not to mention the fact that in the course of their activities they had flattened my best peonies. And I shudder to recall what they'd done to My aubergines. All this I had let pass.

But there is a point beyond which even I will not go.

I had laid down only one rule when I allowed

18. One would tend to agree that The Author is a Merciful God. Mainly because the last person who disagreed is now a small, rather dull cactus in the middle of the Negev Desert.

Adam the free run of the place – neither he nor his wife were to eat of the fruit from the big tree in the middle of the herbaceous border. I told them quite specifically that this was The Tree of Life.[19]

When I laid down this rule I thought that My order was clearly understood. I did not consider it necessary to nail a notice on the tree saying: "God's Apples! Do Not Eat Or Else!" Or "Scrumpers Will Be Prosecuted." Mind you, it wouldn't have done any good as Adam and Eve had not yet got around to inventing language – apart from a series of grunts that meant "Do you fancy a bit of begatting?" – let alone mastered reading. At this point in human development if I showed them a notice they'd have attempted to either eat it or use it as an advanced begatting aid. (I suppose it is a measure of human development that if I showed you a notice today you'd print it on T-shirts or buy the video rights.)[20]

I knew as soon as Adam attempted to cover his parts that My order had been disobeyed. Until he had eaten of the fruit of My tree he didn't know he was naked, he didn't know anything much apart from begatting. The only thing he knew – or was supposed to know – was that he shouldn't eat My apples. In fact, he was so ignorant that I was surprised he actually

19. Also known as The Tree of Good and Evil and thought by experts to be a superior species of the Cox's Orange Pippin.

20. A range of T-shirts will shortly be available, including "God Says ... Repent!". Also watch out for "God: End Of The World Tour" jackets. Video rights are also available, and Andrew Lloyd Webber is bidding to make the musical of the video of the T-shirts. Although The Author is resisting, "I may be Merciful but I find it difficult to forgive what he did to My son's story."

managed to put the apple in his mouth and hadn't tried to use it as a primitive rectal thermometer.

What I wanted to know was why Adam had disobeyed Me and after the dock leaf had soothed his pain, he told Me the story.[21]

It seems that Eve had become an enthusiastic begatter, so enthusiastic that Adam started to feel distinctly peaky and moaned piteously every time she nudged him in the ribs. This was partly because he was still recovering from his recent ribectomy, and partly because he was suffering from the world's first double rupture plus multiple lacerations caused by her insistence on trying to begat while hanging upside down from a cactus.

Eve quickly became irritated by his lack of response and took to wandering around Eden to find whether there was anyone else with whom to begat. Having failed in this endeavour, she got bored and tried to discover whether there was anything as good as or better than begatting.

According to Adam, one afternoon in the course of her wanderings she got into idle conversation with a snake who just happened to be hanging around. They chatted about this and that and the snake finally brought the conversation round to the apples on My tree. It seems he managed to persuade her that they had powerful aphrodisiac qualities which would work wonders on Adam's flagging energies. And she was

---

21. There is some confusion here. The Author has stated that Adam's grasp of language was primitive at best, and yet they conversed. When asked, The Author said they communicated telepathically. "I read Adam's mind, the work of but seconds."

sorely tempted. So she plucked one, took a bite, ran back to her man and told him to eat it.

Adam, being too exhausted to argue, also took a bite and thus committed Original Sin.

Obviously, I had no alternative but to fire Adam and Eve from the Garden Centre. Deafening My ears to their pleas, I cast them forth and slammed the gates behind them.

I watched them stumble off, naked and forlorn, and as they entered the wilderness, Adam turned to Me and said, "All of this for one lousy apple! If I'd known You'd take this attitude I'd have done something *really* naughty!"

And I spake unto him and said: "This is your punishment for disobeying the word of the Lord Thy God. But what really gets up My nose is that you actually expected me to believe all that rubbish about a talking snake."

After The Fall ...

After The Fall came The Winter. And that came as a nasty shock to Adam and Eve because in the Garden Centre they'd got used to a warm climate and it took them a while to find some suitable covering for their nakedness. Adam had particular problems and after several experiments with various bits of greengrocery, including holly and poison ivy – which had disastrous effects on his begatting – was set to give up. It was Eve who discovered fig leaves were far less painful. She attempted to attach three of them to her body but they kept falling off. This had a remarkably therapeutic effect on his begatting because every time they fell, Adam felt one of his urges and, consequently, in the spring Eve gave birth to a child.

They called him Cain, not a particularly

attractive name, but he wasn't a particularly attractive child. Perhaps his least attractive trait was his tendency to murder people. To be fair, he only killed one person, his brother Abel (where do they find these names?) but as there were only four people on Earth at the time he did, effectively, remove a quarter of the population, making him, proportionately, the worst mass murderer in all history.

At first Cain pleaded innocent of the crime. Until I pointed out that the list of suspects consisted of three. And two of them, to wit his mother and father, had cast-iron alibis, being engaged, as they were, in populating the Earth, which involved round-the-clock begatting. Faced with this evidence he finally cracked, admitted his crime and entered as mitigation the fact that he came from a broken home. I overruled this on the grounds that, in My opinion, a couple of rocks under a tree didn't constitute a hovel, let alone a home. And anyway, it was only broken because he had smashed it in a fit of temper. He then tried to plead self-defence, claiming that Abel had attacked him with a lupin.

I pointed out that if Cain thought a lupin was a deadly weapon, he'd do better to plead insanity but even that wouldn't get him far because he was as sane as the next man, even given that the next man was Adam. Which wasn't saying much.

I had no choice but to find Cain guilty. My first impulse was to put him on the wrong end of a thunderbolt, but as this would further deplete the population and, because he hadn't tried to blame a snake for his crime, I decided to be merciful and exiled him to The Land of Nod. Wherein he dwelt, tilling the earth and telling anyone he met, "My name's Cain, I'm the world's first murderer. Not many people know that."[22]

In the meantime life outside Eden continued as usual. Adam and Eve multiplied and begat many sons including Seth who was born when they were 130 years old. They also had daughters who are not mentioned at all in The Bible, probably because they were all called Eve except for their last born girl who was given the name Stanley.[23]

For the next eight hundred years all was peace in My Creation. Adam spent his days delving the ground, hewing wood and drawing water and his nights begatting. Sometimes, for a change, he would begat during the day and delve during the night. And, on other occasions, he would attempt to draw wood and hew water. Very occasionally he would attempt to begat with wood. And when he wasn't doing any of that he was teaching his hundreds of children everything he

22. The land of Nod; this does not mean The Author sent him to sleep. Nod was a country East of Eden next to The Land of Wink. For many years the descendants of Cain disputed with the inhabitants of Wink as to which country was the better. Eventually a Nod fought in single combat against a Wink to decide the issue. Unfortunately the Wink turned up drunk – he became known as the first tiddley wink – and was easily beaten. So, contrary to popular belief, a Wink is not as good as a Nod, even to a blind horse.

23. When asked whether Stanley was originally a girl's name, The Author replied: "No. Adam was a good begatter but he was terrible at thinking up names. He also had thirty-two sons and a pet log called Stanley. He befriended a lump of wood and took it everywhere with him. He used to throw dogs for it to fetch and could never understand why it didn't retrieve them. Looking at Adam I'm amazed that the human race ever developed beyond the Stone Age. Frankly, Eve was the brains of the family and it was she who wore the trousers. Mostly because he could never grasp that he shouldn't put both feet into the same leg."

knew, which was not particularly taxing for either him or the children.

And eventually it came to pass that Adam died, at the age of 930, from terminal boredom.

As for Eve, she lived on to see her great-great-great-great-great-great-great-great-great-great-great-great-great-great-great-great-great-great-grandson, Sheldon, grow to be a man and become the world's first chartered vegetable and tax consultant.[24]

After this crushing disappointment she lost the will to live and I carried her off to Heaven where she resides to this day, greeting souls at The Pearly Gates with the words, "I am Eve, the Mother of the Human Race, have some chicken noodle soup. But first, tell me, how come you didn't write?"

24. The Author obviously means he was a chartered accountant. See footnote 8.

Avant Le Déluge[25]

In all the planets in all the galaxies in all the constellations of the fifteen universes I have never created a lifeform so troublesome, quarrelsome and downright disagreeable as you jumped-up anthropoids on Earth. No sooner have I laid down the Seven Deadly Sins than you've broken them and are committing others that hadn't even occurred to Me. It started early with one of the great-great-great-et cetera-grandchildren of Adam, a nasty piece of work called Mahalameehal. By the time he'd reached puberty he'd got through Pride, Anger, Envy, Lust, Gluttony and Avarice; the only Deadly Sin he hadn't committed was

25. Before The Flood. One suspects The Author is showing off again.

Sloth and that was because he was far too busy with the others to be lazy.

I never had these problems with the Zeugons – a nice, peaceable race on the fourth planet to the left of the fifth galaxy of the seventh universe. They are so law-abiding that I only had to give them One Deadly Sin – I expressly forbade them to have carnal knowledge with woodlice. And not one Zeugon ever disobeyed me. The fact that there were no woodlice on Zeugo is beside the point.

Why couldn't you be more like Zeugons? No sooner had Cain committed fratricide than his relatives were indulging in every form of sin, crime, vice and perversion. If I live to be a thousand – which I will and, indeed, have – I will never understand why you couldn't be content with tending your gardens. To an extent I blame myself for not bestowing My own infinite patience on you.

In those early days people lived longer than they do now. Methuselah was the oldest man who ever lived. He was 969 when he died and while that is no great age as compared to Mine, it's a lot for a simple-minded bipedal with a low boredom threshold.

Not that Methuselah was a sinner, he lived an exemplary life but I felt sorry for him; the poor man was driven to distraction by being constantly asked the secret of his longevity. And having to repeat time and again that he put it down to the complete absence of cigarettes, alcohol, high cholesterol food and traffic accidents. His was a sad death, he was burned to a cinder attempting to blow out all the candles on his 970th birthday cake.

Most of his contemporaries, faced with years and years of nothing much to do – and yet knowing that

however long they lived they'd never survive to see the introduction of the video recorder, personal stereo or vibro-massager – made their own entertainment such as theft, mugging, arson and rape.

To be absolutely honest – and I can't be anything else – although I was vaguely aware of their hobbies I'd rather neglected Earth. I think I must have taken forty winks one afternoon and woke to discover that several hundred years had passed and that things had got out of hand.

I am not easily shocked – after all, there is nothing I haven't seen – but looking down upon the Earth I was shaken by the evil I perceived in the hearts of men. The whole planet was populated by villainy and corruption, My glorious Creation was besmirched and soiled. Sin of every type flourished and wickedness reigned throughout the lands of the world. The entire globe was like one enormous Las Vegas, but without its hideous neon signs. Even this did nothing to mollify Me.

I was moved to great wrath and I said to Myself: "I will destroy man whom I have created from the face of the Earth; both man, and beast, and the creeping thing, and the fowls of the air; for it repenteth me that I have made them." Actually, that's what the scribes who wrote The Bible say I said. A bit florid because they liked to make Me sound pompous, which I'm not. In fact, My own phrase was rather pithier but the gist was the same. I decided to wipe the whole lot out and start again. Now, you see, I've admitted I made a mistake – not easy for a Supreme Being – and would a pompous God do that?[26]

26. "The creeping thing." Most scholars interpret this as referring to the snake. But, as we shall see, The Author was referring to the quug.

Having decided to exterminate all these humans and beasts and fowls, not to mention the creeping thing, I had to decide how best to effect their removal. My preference has always been for the judiciously targeted Intercontinental Ballistic Thunderbolt; as a long-range weapon it can hardly be equalled – it's quick, it's clean and it's accurate. Well, mostly it's accurate, occasionally there's a small mishap – I remember doing some target practice over the barren wastes of North America and I slightly misjudged the power of My bolt. Unfortunate, but I'm told the Grand Canyon is now very popular with tourists.

However, the thunderbolt is only really effective against individual targets, one miserable sinner picked out among a crowd. Tremendously impressive, it puts the fear of Me into any spectator. But for the task in hand I needed something that would wipe out hundreds of thousands and frankly I didn't have the time or the inclination to pick them off one at a time.

The obvious answer was something that would cover the whole Earth and do the job in one fell swoop. Something a bit classier than a plague of boils but not as ostentatious as a full-scale holocaust, which leaves the most appalling mess to be cleared up. Looking at My arsenal, I finally plumped for rain.

As I think I may possibly have mentioned before, I am a Merciful God.[27] And so before I turned on the taps I thought I'd give the world one more chance. Frankly, I slightly regretted My hasty decision to wipe every living thing off the face of the Earth – the beasts and the fowls and even the creeping thing had done nothing to offend Me and the various greengroceries

27. The Author has, in fact, mentioned this before. And one is still inclined to agree with Him.

were utterly innocent, even the cacti had their good points![28]

If I destroyed them I'd only have to go to all the bother of creating them again. So I decided to have a quick recce to see if there was any human worth sparing.

Which is how I found Noah. He was just an ordinary chap but he'd lived a good, honest life with his wife, Norah. If I have one criticism of him it is that at the age of five hundred he'd only fathered three children which shows that he and Norah hadn't been doing their share of begatting but nobody's perfect, except Me, and apparently Norah Noah was a martyr to migraines, which must have cramped his style somewhat. Also, although it was regrettable that they'd named their offspring Japhet, Shem and Ham, I couldn't really count this a sin. Still, I do think Ham is a damned stupid name and later I prohibited the Children of Israel from having anything to do with it. Typically, they went too far and wouldn't even eat the stuff.

I looked into Noah's heart and saw it was pure and I decided that he and his little family would be spared the inundation. So, one evening, as he was cultivating his garden while most of the neighbours were out enjoying themselves at the Rape, Loot And Plunder Club – it was, if I recall, their Strip Bingo and Ladies' Pillage Night – I spake gently unto Noah, not wishing to alarm him.

"Noah", I spake, "This is The Lord Thy God!"

But answer came there none.

---

28. It seems The Author is making a joke. And a very funny one too. Remember, being turned into a cactus is even less amusing.

And again I spake unto him, saying, "Noah, I am The Lord Thy God!"

Still no answer. And yet a third time I spake: "Noah! This is the Lord Thy God speaking."

And this time Noah looked up and beheld Me and he spake unto Me saying, "I don't know who you are but you'll have to speak up because I'm a bit deaf."

So I raised My voice slightly, but not so much as to start the oceans slopping and the mountains trembling or so that we could be overheard by any busybodies. And I spake unto him again saying, "Noah, I am The Lord Thy God, do you understand what I am saying unto you?"

And Noah looked up again and spake, saying, "About half-past-six. Sorry I can't be more accurate than that but the digital watch hasn't been invented yet."

And once more I spake, louder this time, saying "I'm not asking you the time. I'm telling you that I am The Lord Thy God!"

And Noah said, "All right, you don't have to shout. If there's one thing I can't stand, it's people who go around acting as though they're God."

And that is when, in My infinite wisdom, I decided that Noah could drown with the rest of them.

The Ark

I'm not sure if I've mentioned this before, but if I'm nothing else, I am a Merciful God. Having left Noah to his fate I fell to pondering that I'd been a trifle impatient with him. After all, a certain deafness is only to be expected in a 500-year-old man. As I get older I, Myself, find it harder to hear everything that's said to Me. I do wish you wouldn't mumble when you say your prayers, it makes My job so much harder. Not that many of you do say your prayers any more; unless you're really in trouble and then you can't get on your knees fast enough, can you? Well, I do object to being treated like some cosmic insurance policy – you don't like paying your premiums, but you're quick enough to call on Me when something goes seriously wrong. The next time you want My help, I suggest you read the

small print – especially the clause that refers to "Act of God" and which states that God will only act if you're fully paid up. Or, rather, fully prayed up![29]

Where was I? Ah, yes, Noah. I reconsidered My rather hasty decision and gave him another chance. So I returned the next evening and before attempting to communicate with him again I blew in his ear and cured his deafness.[30]

And I spake unto him saying, "Noah, can you hear Me?"

And he jumped out of his seat and said, "Oh! My God! You scared me half to death."

And I said "Yes, Noah, I *am* your God."

He said, "Pull the other one, it's got bells on it."

And I looked around and saw neither bells nor anything to pull. And I said, "You speak in riddles, Noah. Look at Me and be not afraid."

And Noah looked at Me and gazed upon My majesty and said unto Me, "I truly believe you are God."

And I said to him, "Yes, Noah, I am."

And he said, "Somehow I thought You'd be taller."

And I told him My intentions: "I am sickened by the depravity that stalks My Creation and I have decided to wash it all away. Shortly there will be torrential rains that will last for forty days and forty

29. Another example of The Author's highly developed sense of humour. If anything, this joke is even more rib-tickling than His last.

30. In the light of what The Author has written about His own partial hearing loss, the editor asked Him why He didn't perform a similar miracle on Himself. He replied: "A miracle is one thing, but have you ever tried blowing in your own ear?"

nights and will cause a great flood that will cover the Earth. And everything upon the face of the Earth will be destroyed. Everything, that is, except you and your family."

And Noah looked at Me and said, "Rain? We never get rain in these parts at this time of year".

And I scowled at Noah and he, seeing My displeasure, said, "All right, keep Your halo on. You're the boss, if You say it's going to rain, that's fine by me. So what do You want me to do?"

And I told him. And when I had finished, he spake unto Me, saying: "Let's see if I've got this right. You want me to build an ark 300 cubits long by 50 cubits wide by 30 cubits high, made of best quality gopher wood and lined inside and out with pitch. Is that correct?"

"Yes, Noah, that is correct."

And Noah said, "Fine. I can't see any problems. Apart from the fact that I can't even put up a shelf straight. And that my garden, in which You want me to build this bloody great boat, is only 20 cubits long and 15 cubits wide. And that I, a 500-year-old man with a bad back, am supposed to do all this single-handed, without help from anyone, not even Ham who knows a bit about D.I.Y., having successfully erected his own carousel washing line.

"I don't suppose it ever occurred to You, in Your infinite wisdom, to give the job to a firm of professional boat-builders?"

And I spake unto him, saying, "I have chosen you, Noah, for this task. I will give you the strength and skill to complete the work. Have faith in Me. Did I not cure you of your deafness?"

And Noah looked up at Me and spake unto Me, saying, "Pardon?"

And I was sorely vexed by Noah until he said, "It was just a joke. Haven't You got a sense of humour?"

And I laughed and said, "Indeed, I do have a sense of humour, Noah!" And to prove it, I turned him into a cactus.

Having enjoyed My little joke, I restored Noah to his natural form and he went away rejoicing. He ran to his wife saying, "Norah, it is going to rain for forty days and forty nights."

And Norah replied, "Really, dear? Well I expect the garden could do with it."

And then he told her, "And I'm going to build an ark 300 cubits long and 50 cubits wide and 30 cubits high."

And she replied, saying, "That's nice, dear, every man should have a hobby."

And Noah said, "You don't understand, I have been vouchsafed this task by God Himself."

And she replied, "Of course you have, dear. Now wash your hands before supper."

And he said, "I'm not even going to bother telling you about the cactus."

Le Déluge[31]

Noah toiled long and hard on the ark. It took him a hundred years, far longer than I had intended but it wasn't his fault, he had to wait seventy years for planning permission from the local council.

As he built it people journeyed from far and wide and marvelled at the structure, saying, "Verily, it is a huge garden shed. When it is finished it will be even bigger than that owned by The Jonahs next door." While others scoffed, saying "Verily, he is only trying to keep up with The Jonahses."[32]

And to those that mocked, Noah merely said,

31. The Flood: when asked why He'd rendered this into French, The Author said, "John-Paul's not the only one who can speak fluently in tongues".

32. "Verily" appears to have been a popular name in those days.

"Sticks and stones may break my bones, but words will never hurt me."

Hearing this, the mockers were amazed and stopped hurling scornful words at him and hurled sticks and stones instead. But still did My good and faithful servant continue with his task, even in plaster.

Eventually it was finished and I made a tour of inspection. I saw that he had made it of good gopher wood, that he had lined it with pitch both inside and out and that, as I had ordained, its dimensions were 300 cubits by 50 cubits by 30 cubits.[33]

I congratulated Noah on his work, saying, "Well done! But why did you paint it bright pink?"

And he said, "That was the wife's idea. Personally I favoured something less garish but she insisted that it matched the curtains." And then he said, "Lord, I have built this ark as You ordained, except for the colour which I admit is definitely on the lurid side. I have toiled at this task for a hundred years which is a long time and I've completely forgotten what the bloody thing is for."

And again I told him of the great inundation and how the ark would save him and his family from extinction. And he said, "Lord, there is only me and my wife;

33. A cubit was the measure taken from the length of the arm, from the elbow to the tip of the middle finger. It was rather imprecise, ranging from 18 to 22 inches, depending on the height of the workman. Assuming Noah was of average height, the dimensions of the ark would be approximately 150 yards long by 25 yards wide by 15 yards high. Or 450 feet long by 75 feet wide by 45 feet high. Or 137.16 metres long by 22.86 metres wide by 13.72 metres high. On the other hand, The Bible (Genesis vi, 4) states, "There were giants in the earth in those days". So it could have been much bigger. When asked to clarify this point, The Author said, "Who cares?".

our sons, Shem and Japhet and their wives, and their children Sharon, Darren, Karen and Warren. Not forgetting Ham and his wife and their children Bacon, Pork and little Chipolata. This is a very large ark for fifteen people."

And I said, "Noah, do not forget the animals."

And he said, "Animals? What animals? You never mentioned any animals."

And I said, "Well, I thought you had enough to be doing without worrying about the animals." And I told him of My plan.

And Noah spake unto Me, saying, "Let me see if I've got this right. You want me to travel throughout the known world and catch two specimens of every living animal, one male and one female, from the aardvark to the zorro, whatever they may be. Even though I am allergic to animal fur which brings me out in a plague of boils.

"Then You want me to catch each and every fowl of the earth, the beasts of the field, the insects and amphibia, not forgetting the creeping thing. And when I've caught them, You want me to bring them back here and herd them into the ark. Is that correct?"

"Yes, Noah, that is correct."

And Noah said, "And You want me to do all this in seven days?"

"Yes Noah, that is correct."

And Noah said, "Has anyone ever told You You're out of Your mind?"

And I said, "How would you like to be a cactus?"

And he said, "Well, I can't sit around here chit-chatting to You, I've got animals to catch." And he went on his way praising My name, saying, "God Almighty! What a job!"

After seven days, Noah returned to the ark with two of every animal that lived upon the Earth from the aardvark to the zorro, not forgetting the creeping thing which was called the quug. And people journeyed from far and wide and marvelled, saying, "Typical! Noah's showing off again. If he wants some pets why couldn't he be content with a couple of hamsters?"

But Noah ignored them and led the animals into the ark and gave them food and water, and I commanded the animals to abide on the ark in peace. Hearing My words, the lion lay down with the lamb, the tiger lay down with the kid and the elephant lay down on the quug. Which halved the entire quug population.

And after he had settled the animals, Noah took his family into the ark and as night fell on the seventh day he stood on the deck of the ark with his wife and gazed into the sky and said, "It looks like it might rain."

And she said, "How can you tell?"

And he said, "Because my arthritis is giving me gyp. And because God told me."

And she said, "Nothing like a spot of rain to freshen the place up. Now, do you fancy a nice quug steak for your dinner?"

And lo, I ordained a great and torrential rain. And it rained for forty days and forty nights and everything on the Earth was consumed by the flood waters. And nothing lived on the Earth except those that were in the ark. And for forty days and forty nights the ark bobbed on the surface of the waters.

And for forty mornings Noah looked out of the ark and said, "Guess what? It's still raining."

And for forty mornings Shem said, "Which idiot forgot to pack the seasickness pills?"

And for forty nights Japhet said, "Not quug soup for supper again! Surely God wouldn't miss just one chicken."

And for forty nights Japhet said, "Who's for another game of I Spy? I'll start. I spy with my little eye something beginning with 'R'."

And for forty nights Ham said, "Got it! Rain!"

And for forty nights their wives said to them, "You don't really expect any begatting? Not when I've got one of my migraines. And is it any surprise what with the smell of those animals?"

And for forty days and forty nights Mrs Noah said, "There's nothing like a sea cruise to blow away the cobwebs."

And on the forty-first day, all the rest of them said, "If she says that one more time we'll throw her overboard."

And it was on the forty-first day that I caused the rains to cease. But the ark continued to sail on the waters for another one hundred and fifty days because I was fed up with all their moaning.

And after a while Noah sent forth a raven.

And the raven had a note tied to its leg saying:

Dear God,

Is it all right if we leave the ark?
Yours sincerely,

Noah.

P.S. The weather here is fine, but it rained for the whole of the first forty days and forty nights.
P.P.S. What are we supposed to do with all this animal manure?

And I wrote a note back saying:

Dear Noah,

The waters have not yet abated. Have you any idea how long it takes to drain a whole planet of flood water?
Stay where you are.
You remain my obedient servant,

God,
P.S. Re the manure. You think you've got problems. I've got to find a way to shift a whole planet full of mud.
P.P.S. Don't you know that a raven is not a homing bird?

The raven, not being a homing bird, never returned to the ark. So Noah sent forth a dove with another note saying:

Dear God,

Why didn't You answer our last letter? Can we get off the ark now? We are up to our knees in manure. Also the animals have started begatting. It's getting very crowded, there's not room to swing a cat. So for entertainment, Sharon, Karen, Darren and Warren are having to swing a guinea pig.
We're getting desperately short of food.
Please write soon,

Noah.
P.S. While not questioning Your infinite wisdom, I am beginning to wonder whether bringing two woodworm on board was a good idea.

78

I sent the dove back and gave it an olive leaf to carry as a sign. Two days later it returned with another message:

Dear God,

The dove just arrived but seems to have lost its letter. The airmail system isn't all it's cracked up to be. However, it did bring an olive leaf for which many thanks. But, frankly, olive leaf pie doesn't go very far between 15 people. Position is getting desperate. I don't like the way Shem and Japhet keep looking at their brother and saying, "I really fancy a Ham sandwich".

Help!

Noah.

P.S. Since writing the above, Ham has taken matters into his own hands. Instead of sending forth another bird he decided to send forth the one remaining quug by hurling it out of the window to hear if it made a splash or a splat when it landed. After it went splat we concluded that the waters had abated and decided to venture outside.

We seem to have landed on the top of a mountain. Very tricky situation with the ark delicately balanced and in danger of crashing over, especially if the elephants make any unexpected moves. We are fearful for our lives. Please come quickly.

P.P.S. Mrs Noah says the view is very nice.

The trouble with being Me is that people are

always expecting Me to do the impossible. Not unfair, I suppose, because, of course, I can do the impossible.[34]

But I do wish people wouldn't treat Me as though I was some comic book superhero. However, I did answer Noah's plea – without the advantage of being able to use a telephone booth as a changing room, but as there was no one around to see Me get out of My pyjamas it didn't matter – and made sure the ark was stable by supporting it on My little finger and watched as he checked the animals off.

There were two of everything from the aardvark to the zorro, except for the quug of which there were none. In addition, there were 14 rats, several dozen mice, 23,000 rabbits and countless billion fleas which begat at a rate which surpised even Me. It took days to get them out of My beard; I wish I'd let the wretched things drown. Sometimes I'm too merciful for My own good.[35]

34. According to what The Author said in footnote 30, regarding blowing in His own ear, it seems that occasionally the impossible defeats even Him. When asked again about this point, He said, "Of course, I can blow into My own ear. I've just never got around to it". Whether this is another of The Author's little jokes is not clear.

35. When asked what the quug, or creeping thing, looked like, The Author said, "It was small, flat and completely covered in turquoise hair. Its nearest existing relative is the fluffy toilet seat cover. It had some extremely distressing personal habits of which emitting a vile odour and attacking dangly bits of unsuspecting males were only two. All-in-all it was no great loss. Though it's a pity about the bandlecroot, a delightful little creature that resembled the koala bear. Unfortunately, being an incredibly slow mover, it was overtaken by all the other animals including the tortoises and arrived at the ark three hours after Noah had locked the doors. A great loss to wildlife documentary makers and soft toy manufacturers."

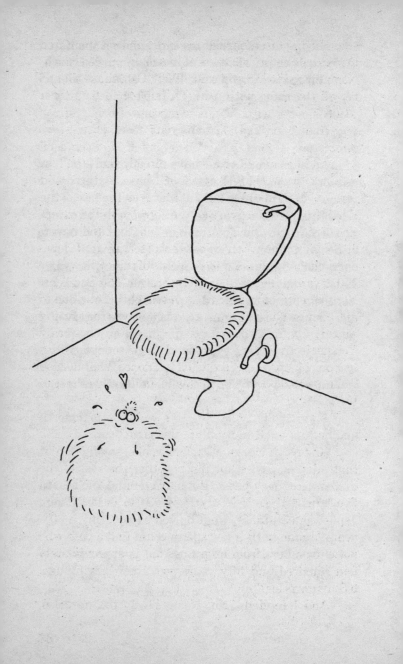

Having disembarked his cargo and set them free to roam the empty vastness of the newly purged Earth, Noah turned to Me and said, "Well, God, that's that. If it's all the same with You, I'll put my feet up for a while."

And I replied, "Noah your task is not yet complete."

And he said, "Lord, I have already built the biggest ark the world will ever see. I have captured and carefully tended every animal that is on the face of the Earth from the aardvark to the zorro, with the exception of the quug and, according to You, the bandlecroot, although I don't remember ever seeing it. I have endured forty days and forty nights of rain, followed by 150 days and nights plagued by hunger, fear and fleas. Not to mention breaking out in unsightly boils due to my allergy and suffering in other ways from eating rancid quug meat which was not made any better by You neglecting to incorporate adequate toilet facilities in Your blueprints. All this have I done. What do You want me to do now? Move this mountain three feet to the left?"

And I replied, "No, Noah, I want you to go forth and multiply and re-populate the earth."

And Noah looked at me and spake, saying "Oh, is that all! You just want me to father the rest of the human race! Easy-peasy! But may I remind You that in five hundred years I only managed to father Shem, Japhet and Ham. So what do you expect from a 601-year-old man with a low sperm count and a wife who not only suffers from migraines but is approximately four hundred and fifty years past child-bearing age, bloody miracles?"

And I replied, "No, Noah, I'll do the miracles,

including turning you into a cactus if you don't get on with the multiplying."

And Noah saw the wisdom in this and called unto him his wife, Norah, saying, "Don't bother to get dressed, we've got some begatting to do."

And she said unto him in return, "Have you been talking to God again?"

"Yes, He wants us to fill the Earth with children."

And she said, "Oh, well, at least it's a nice day for it."

Thus it came to pass that Noah begat and when he wasn't begatting he tended the soil and tried to raise a vineyard.

I was well pleased with My servant and to reward him I gave him the rainbow, saying, "Noah, this is My gift to you."

Noah gazed at the beauty of the rainbow and said, "Very nice, I'm sure, but why couldn't you give me something useful?"

And I replied, saying, "Noah, you are a good man and a faithful servant, but at heart you are a philistine."[36]

"That's all very well," he said, "but what I really want to know is, what I'm supposed to do with a hundred thousand tons of animal manure."

And I told Noah exactly what he could do with it. Which is how Noah raised the most fertile vineyard that ever grew.

He lived for another three hundred years but begat no more children because Mrs Noah made him sleep in a separate room due to the fact that however much he bathed he could never get rid of the smell.

36. The Author adds: "But not as big a Philistine as Goliath."

Après Le Déluge

There was a great deal of begatting after that and before long Noah's children's children's children started getting ideas above their station. Some, for example, attempted to build the world's first skyscraper in a town called Babel. A stupid idea, particularly as they hadn't yet invented the elevator – nobody was going to pay the rents they were asking when it took three days to climb the stairs from the lobby to the penthouse.

The Bible blames Me for destroying it but you shouldn't take everything The Bible says as gospel, except The Gospels, of course. I never touched the tower; I've got better things to do than go around as a cosmic demolition contractor. Its destruction was due to human greed, the builder was involved in a crooked

SOME OF GOD'S WONDERS

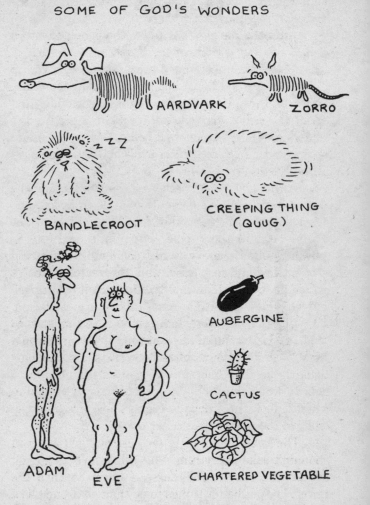

AARDVARK

ZORRO

BANDLECROOT

CREEPING THING
(QUUG)

AUBERGINE

CACTUS

ADAM

EVE

CHARTERED VEGETABLE

deal with his brother-in-law – who supplied substandard bricks – and the thing simply collapsed under its own weight. Forty-six estate agents were killed in the accident, so some good came of it.

After the Babelgate scandal, the people involved fled to the four corners of the Earth to escape arrest. They settled in unpopulated areas, set themselves up as vegetables and flourished by cheating each other. However, the law eventually caught up with them and when the police arrived they pretended they didn't understand a word that was being said to them and spoke gibberish in return, which is how the languages of the Earth were invented.[37]

Although I didn't knock over The Tower of Babel, I did, of course, issue a demolition order on Sodom and Gomorrah which were known as The Cities of the Plain, because the people living in them were so physically unattractive. Sadly, their ugliness did not stop them indulging in vile and perverted practices which gave their names to the unnatural acts of sodomy and gomorrahy.[38]

I can't recall whether I've previously mentioned that I am a Merciful God. But even My mercy can only be stretched so far, and having wiped all wickedness

37. "Vegetables" are, of course, accountants. This is an interesting revelation about the development of human languages. And may explain why, to this day, most people can't understand a word accountants are saying.

38. "Sodomy" needs no explanation. If it does, consult any standard textbook, good dictionary or average work of pornography. However, the word "gomorrahy" has fallen into disuse. When asked about the act of gomorrahing, The Author was vague but seemed to imply it was a sexual practice involving a goat, an aubergine and a rubber sink plunger.

from The Earth only a few generations previously, I was furious when I discovered that some of you anthropoids were up to your old tricks and, indeed, some new tricks which Adam's great-great-great-etc-grandchildren hadn't discovered. So when one of my contacts in Sodom, a man called Lot – a silly name given by his father who on hearing that he had just had his seventeenth son and twenty-eighth child said, "That's the lot" – told Me what was going on, I decided to investigate for Myself.

Now, obviously, when I descend to Earth I don't go around in a flowing robe that looks like a nightshirt, wearing a halo round My head. It makes Me too conspicuous, especially at night when I am frequently mistaken for a lamppost, especially by dogs. I adopt a different form depending on the situation, sometimes as an anthropoid like yourselves, sometimes as an animal and sometimes as an inanimate object; kindly remember that the next time you stick your chewing gum on the underside of a cinema seat.

For My visits to Sodom and Gomorrah I decided to manifest Myself as an insurance agent, in which guise I could go from house-to-house, from business-to-business, under the pretext of selling My policies.

This was a good ploy because both Sodom and Gomorrah were bustling towns full of small businesses, mostly bars, restaurants and clubs. I went from one den of iniquity to another, each more lascivious and disgusting than the last. And in every place I got the same response. Nobody was interested in insurance – they would soon wish they'd listened more carefully to My sales pitch – and everywhere I went strange men asked Me to dance.

I shall not attempt to describe the appalling sinks and stews of Sodom and Gomorrah.[39] Suffice it to say they were like Hell on Earth. The heat, the noise, but worst of all, the people.[40]

I did not need to spend long in these cities of sin to realize that drastic action would have to be taken. Being a Merciful God, before I razed them to the ground I visited Lot to warn him of My decision, but he slammed the door in My face, saying, "I've got all the insurance I need."

39. "Sinks and Stews": the Author is using them in their arcane form, meaning brothels and disorderly houses. Not a reference to either the catering or plumbing found in Sodom and Gomorrah. However, He adds that the hygiene in most of the restaurants did leave much to be desired, especially in Gomorrah where all available sink plungers were being put to another purpose. But the food was surprisingly good. Especially in a little bistro called "Big Boys" which, He recalls, "Served the best mess of pottage I've ever eaten, almost worth Esau selling his birthright for it. I only wish I'd got the recipe before I closed the place down."

40. It seems as though The Author is comparing Hell to a disco. After some thought, He admitted that this wasn't an accurate analogy as some people actually seem to enjoy being crammed into small, hot, stinking holes while being subjected to Grace Jones records played at painfully high volume. He maintains that Hell is even worse than this. A barren, bleak and inhospitable place, where crowds of lost, bewildered souls wander aimlessly through Eternity, gnashing their teeth and bewailing their misfortunes, while being tormented by shrieking devils. In fact, very like the departure lounge of an international airport where the planes never arrive, the restaurants are always closed and the queue for the toilets never diminishes and where Grace Jones records are perpetually played at painfully high volume. He said He can't imagine anything worse except listening to Grace Jones records played at painfully high volume on a wet Sunday in November in Belgium.

And I spake unto him, saying, "But I am the man who insured your great-great-etc-grandfather, Noah, against flood."

And he said, "I've heard it all before. Yesterday, a man came round claiming he's sold single glazing to my brother Abraham. A ridiculous idea, putting bits of glass into holes in the wall! And anyway, Abraham lives in a tent!"

And I spake unto him again, saying "Lot, are you insured against fire?"

"Of course, I am."

"And what about brimstone and sulphur?"

And he said, "What about it?"

And I said, "There's going to be a lot of it about and I, the Lord Thy God, have decided to save you from it."

And still he would not listen until I had proved My identity by putting on My halo. And when he finally opened the door, he said, "Forgive me, Lord, for my lack of faith. Sorry I didn't recognize You, but somehow I thought You'd be taller. Now come in quickly before some dog mistakes You for a lamppost."

I entered his humble dwelling and told him to take his wife and his daughters and flee. And I told him that as they fled they must not turn nor look backwards. And when he asked why not, I explained that I didn't like people watching Me as I work.

Lot and his wife and his daughters fled in great haste, and when they were well away from Sodom and Gomorrah, I rained down fire and brimstone and sulphur on to The Cities of the Plain and expunged them from the face of the Earth, together with all who dwelt in them. And very enjoyable it was.

But as the cities were being consumed, Lot's wife turned back, saying, "Lot, because you made us leave so

fast, I forgot that I had a cake in the oven." And instantly I turned her into a pillar of salt.

And Lot looked towards Heaven and said, "Why did You do that?"

And I spake, saying, "It is punishment for her disobedience. And if I have any trouble from you, I'll turn you into a pillar of pepper and your daughters into matching condiment pots."

And he said, "All right, all right, there's no need to be ratty, just because You got out of the wrong side of the bed this morning."

And Lot travelled to Zoar where he abided in peace. And he became an object of curiosity in that town because he was the only man who had escaped from Sodom and Gomorrah. And because he was the only man who never took salt on his food, explaining, "You never know who it's been."

Out Of Africa

move in mysterious ways My wonders to perform, remember that the next time you see a man crawling on all fours across the fast lane of the M.25.

One of the more mysterious ways in which I moved was to disguise Myself as a bush in order to have a chat with Moses. It's a mystery even to Me, can't imagine what possessed Me to do it. But, there I was, manifesting Myself as a rather attractive azalea, waiting for Moses to walk past with his sheep.

It just so happens that azalea bushes were extremely rare in Egypt at that time so you'd have thought that Moses, as he strolled along, would have stopped and said to himself, "That's an unusual shrub, you don't see many azalea bushes in ancient Egypt, I'll take a closer look." Or, at the very least, one of his sheep

might have drawn his attention to it by having a nibble at Me and being instantly turned into chump chops.

But did he see Me? No, he walked straight past. So I had no alternative but to burst into flames. A trifle extreme, I agree, although I have occasionally been tempted to try something similar in restaurants. Even when you possess infinite patience it can be extremely irritating trying to catch a waiter's eye. What has the world come to when God Almighty has to consider flambéing Himself before He can order His post-prandial crème de menthe?

So there I was, burning away and calling, "Moses! Moses!" and he just stood, slack-jawed, staring. And I said, "Don't look so stupid, anybody'd think you'd never seen a burning bush before."

And he said, "Who are You?"

And I said, "I am the Lord Thy God. Who do you think I am, Mickey Mouse?"

And he said, "Who's Mickey Mouse?"

And I said, "Don't bother, it'll take far too long to explain. Now come closer so that I can talk to you without shouting."

And he came closer, and stared in wonder and covered his face, saying, "B-b-bloody Ada, I've singed my eyebrows. Could You turn down the heat a b-b-bit."

Eventually, I managed to make him understand that I had chosen him for a special role. "You are to lead the Israelites out of Egypt and into The Land Flowing With Milk And Honey. And you will give them signs so that they will know you have been appointed by Me."

And Moses said, "B-b-but G-g-god, c-c-can't You g-g-get someone else to t-t-tell them? I've g-g-got th-th-this t-t-terrible st-st-st . . ."

And I said, "All right, I can't wait around all day

while you finish the sentence. Get your brother Aaron to tell them instead."

And Moses said, "Th-th-th-tha ..."

"You're welcome. Now go and tell Aaron what to do."

And Moses told Aaron. And when he'd finished, three days later, Aaron called together all the elders of the Israelites and he showed them the signs that I had given to Moses. First he turned his staff into a serpent. Then he showed them his hand and it was leprous, then he showed them it again and it was healed. Lastly, he poured water on to the ground and it turned to blood.

And the elders were amazed and marvelled, saying, "That's really brilliant! Can I book you for my son's bar mitzvah?"

Then Aaron told them how Moses would lead them into The Land Flowing With Milk And Honey. And they said, "We're not going there, it sounds really messy. Imagine the dry cleaning bills!"

But Aaron said, "Is it any worse than being under the whip of the cruel Pharaoh?" And they all agreed it wasn't. All, that is, except Zebediah.[41]

And Aaron said to Moses, "You see, I told you we'd persuade them just as long as you didn't try spinning them that cock-and-bull story about the talking bush."

Moses came to Me, asking what he should do and I told him all that he must do and all that he must say. And Moses went and spake unto Pharaoh saying, "G-g-god has t-t-told m-m-me t-t-to t-t-tell you t-t-to l-l-let m-m-my p-p-people g-g-go". But answer came there none because Pharaoh had fallen alseep. And so Aaron

---

41. Zebediah, proprietor of The Pyramid Go-Go Bar and Massage Parlour, had some strange tastes.

woke him and briefly repeated what Moses had said
and Pharaoh had them thrown out of his palace.

Again they returned. And Moses said, "G-g-god
has t-t-told m-m-me ..." And Pharaoh said, "Yes, I
know, he told you to tell me to let your people go. But I
won't." And so Moses showed him a sign by turning his
staff into a serpent. And Pharaoh said, "Seen it! Can't
you do something really clever like saw a woman in
half?" And they admitted they couldn't, but instead
they turned the Nile into a river of blood. And Pharaoh
said, "Not bad, but it's been done before. How are you at
producing live doves from handkerchiefs?" When they
said they hadn't learned that one, Pharaoh had them
thrown out again.

And eventually Moses called to Me and said, "L-l-
lord, I've d-d-done m-m-my b-b-best t-t-tricks ..."

And I said, "All right, Moses, I know what you're
trying to say."

But Moses interrupted Me and said: "If You're so
c-c-clever why d-d-don't you c-c-cure m-m-my st-st-
stammer?"

So I did. And then I said, "I've had to deal with
some stubborn people in My time, but I admit that
Pharaoh is the most pig-headed. He's left Me with no
alternative but The Plagues."

So I sent a Plague of Frogs, which didn't have the
desired effect because the Egyptians were particularly
partial to grenouille. And still Pharaoh wouldn't let My
people go.[42]

Then I tried plagues of Gnats and Flies, which
may not sound too ghastly to you but remember this
was years before a really effective aerosol insecticide

42. "Grenouille" is the French for frogs' legs. The Author is
    showing off again.

had been developed. Still Pharaoh wouldn't change his mind. Then I tried Boils. Nothing. After that, Hail. And finally Locusts.

But still Pharaoh remained implacable. And My wrath was great and I summoned Moses and told him I was going to send the most terrible plague of all but that if he followed My orders to the letter, this plague would not affect the Israelites.

So Moses departed and told the Israelites what I had ordained and, accordingly, they daubed signs on their doors, so that the plague would pass them over.

And on the appointed night I sent the final horror into Egypt – The Plague of Encyclopaedia Salesmen.

And so it came to pass that they knocked on the door of every Egyptian house but they did not approach the doors daubed by the Israelites. And faced with this terror Pharaoh called Moses and said unto him, "Okay, I know when I'm beaten. You and your people and herds can go, as long as you take those salesmen with you."

And Moses said, "Rejoice in the name of the Lord, for this is the time of our exodus."

And Pharaoh said, "What does 'exodus' mean?"

And Moses replied, "Look it up in your encyclopaedia."

Thus did Moses lead the Children of Israel out of Egypt. Together with the Teenagers of Israel, the Adults of Israel and the Geriatrics of Israel.[43]

43. This account differs significantly from that given in The Bible which maintains that The Author killed the first born son of every Egyptian. When asked, The Author said, "Those Old Testament scribes liked to make Me out as jealous and vengeful. Whereas I am, in fact, a Merciful God. Although it's not something I like to boast about."

Parting The Red Sea And Some Other Of My Better Miracles

'm not given to self-doubt; after all, if I expect everyone to have faith in Me, the least I can do is have faith in Myself. But occasionally, in an idle moment, once in every several millennia, I do wonder about My own infinite wisdom. Take Moses, for example; not only did I pick a man with a speech impediment to speak on My behalf, I also chose this man to lead the Israelites out of Egypt and into The Promised Land. A man with absolutely no sense of direction. He couldn't find the toilet in his own house without a map.

No sooner had he started leading the Israelites out of Egypt than he was leading them back into Egypt. So I spake unto him saying, "Moses, turn around again and head for the banks of the Red Sea."

And he said, "Why didn't You tell me we were going to the seaside, I'd have packed my bucket and spade? Very inconsiderate, I call it. Now, let me think ... the Red Sea ... that's in the Sahara Desert, isn't it?"

So I sent a column of dust ahead of him to guide his way by day and a column of fire to guide his way by night and erected signposts every mile of the way saying "Red Sea Straight On". As The Children of Israel journeyed onwards, they drove their herds before them, until they came to a sign announcing, "The Red Sea Welcomes Careful Drovers". And then Moses led The Children of Israel to the banks of the Red Sea.

The Israelites clustered round him, saying, "Call these banks? There's nowhere we can change our Traveller's Cheques!"

And Moses explained that the banks were but the shores of the sea and they said, "Well, this is a nice spot. Why don't we settle here, open some proper banks, build condominiums and design robes with little alligators on the breast pockets?"

But those at the back of the line – fifteen miles behind – started sending a message to the leaders, saying, "Pharaoh is coming after us with war chariots, and he looks really annoyed. Maybe he doesn't like the way the encyclopaedias were bound in lustrous leather-style vellumette. But what did he expect for the price, hand-tooled morocco?"

When the message reached the head of the line, the Israelites said unto Moses, "On second thoughts, this is a rotten place to build condominiums, we must get out of here. But how will we cross the Red Sea, seeing as there are no boats, nay, not even pedalos?"

And Moses said, "Don't worry, the Lord will part the waters of the sea, so that we can cross."

And I, overhearing this, whispered unto Moses, "How do you expect Me to do that?"

And he said, "You're God, You come up with the answer."

And I said, "I do wish you'd consult Me before making rash promises on My behalf."

And he said, "Why don't You blow on the waters?"

And I said, "I'd remind you that this is the Red Sea, not a cup of hot coffee."

And he said, "You mean You can't do it."

And I said "Of course I can do it, I'm just out of practice at parting seas, that's all."

So I blew mightily upon the Red Sea and the waters parted and the Israelites rushed across. When they were on the opposite bank, I stopped blowing and the waters gushed back again, drowning all the Egyptians and their horses. Which was a bit unfortunate but I was completely out of breath, not being as young as I once was and having a sedentary job in which I don't get enough exercise.

Having been saved from the Egyptians, the Israelites rejoiced, saying, "The Lord has brought us across the Red Sea, which is not as nice as the other side, having less palm trees, a shingle beach and absolutely no water-skiing facilities, but at least there are no Egyptians so I suppose we ought to be thankful for small mercies."

And Moses proposed that they sing "For He's A Jolly Good God" and give three hearty cheers of "Hip, Hip, Hallelujah!" But the Israelites said, "He only deserves two cheers because, after all, we are His chosen people and He was doing no more than His duty. And anyway, we got our shoes wet and who's going to pay for the damage?"

But Miriam took a tambourine and composed a song of praise which went:

> Sing to the Lord,
> For he is highly exalted.
> The horse and its rider
> He has hurled into the sea.[44]

And after feasting and rejoicing and recovering from hangovers, and bickering about who was going to pay for the feasting and rejoicing, Moses again led The Children of Israel towards The Promised Land but, turning right instead of left, found himself in the desert. And the Israelites fell to weeping and wailing and gnashing their teeth, complaining, "This is a dreadful place, the landscape is really boring, there are no decent shops and there is nothing to eat or drink. All-in-all, we'd be better off in Egypt where at least, after a hard day building the pyramids, you got a decent chicken noodle soup."

And Moses calmed them, saying, "The Lord will provide."

And I whispered unto him, "Since when was I in the fast food business?"

---

44. The Author adds: "Not My favourite song about Me, no tune to speak of and the words don't rhyme; it's no wonder that Israel has won The Eurovision Song Contest twice. There have been far better songs praising My name. Without boasting, I've inspired more hit tunes than anyone else. Personally, I prefer something stirring like "God Our Help In Ages Past" or "Abide With Me". Not that many people sing them nowadays, but what can you expect? Religion isn't what it was – talk to most people today about Genesis and they think it's a pop group. And mention My archangel, Gabriel, and they say, "Didn't Phil Collins replace him as the lead singer?"

And he said, "You're supposed to be omnipotent aren't You? All we're asking for is thirty thousand salt beef sandwiches, easy on the mustard; twenty thousand hot pastrami on rye and fifty thousand lox and bagels, half with mayo, half without. And maybe a modest Chablis to wash them down."

And I said, "You'll have what you're given." So I sent them dew to drink and quails and bread from heaven to eat.

And The Children of Israel drank the dew and said, "Well, it slakes the thirst, but Chablis it ain't."

And they caught the quails and consumed them and said, "Call that a square meal? There's hardly enough meat on a quail to keep body and soul together."

And they gathered the bread and ate it and called it "manna", which means "bread from heaven that looks like hailstones and tastes like stale camel blanket."

And I visited Moses and said, "Moses, I have rescued your people from the tyranny of Pharaoh, I have smitten Egypt with plagues, I have delivered you from thine enemies, I have parted the Red Sea and now I have catered for a hundred thousand people at very short notice. And still The Children of Israel complain and moan and bitch. I'm beginning to wonder why I bother with them."

And he spake unto Me, saying, "All these wonders You have wrought because these are Thy chosen people."

And I replied, "Yes, you speak truly. But what I can't work out is why I chose them. Nothing's good enough for them and they're as miserable as sin."

And he said, "Be fair, God, that's just not true. The only thing they don't find miserable is sin."

"Yes, Moses, I was meaning to talk to you about that. There's far too much sinning going on. It's got to stop. I've some Commandments to give you."

And Moses said, "All right, give me a moment to find a pen and paper and I'll jot them down."

"No, Moses, I'm not having you scribbling them on the back of an envelope and losing them. I shall hand down these Commandments on the top of Mount Sinai. Meet Me yonder tomorrow afternoon when I shall descend in glory."

And Moses said, "You are The Lord My God and I will obey. But I think you're making a song and a dance about it."

The Eleven
Commandments

The next day, at the appointed hour, I descended from Heaven on to the summit of Mount Sinai in a cloud of fire, accompanied by thunder and lightning and the sound of celestial trumpets.

And I spake in a great voice, that caused Sinai to tremble and quake, saying, "Moses! This is The Lord Thy God and here are My Commandments."

And there was an awesome silence.

And I spake again, saying, "Moses! Where the hell are you?"

And three hours later Moses finally arrived, saying, "Sorry I'm late but I must have taken the wrong turning."

And yet again I spake, and My voice was as thunder:

"I am The Lord Thy God, which have brought thee out of the land of Egypt, out of the house of bondage."[45]

And Moses said, "Yes, I know all that. Can we skip the introductions and get on to the important bit. And You don't have to shout, I'm not deaf."

And I said, "Moses, it's a good job I'm a Merciful God or else I would smite thee hip and thigh. I have written My Commandments on these tablets of stone. Read them, understand them and live your life according to them."

And Moses read them and said, "Number One: 'Thou Shalt Have No Other Gods Before Me.' 'Shalt', what sort of word is 'shalt?' "

"Moses, I'm warning you ... hip and thigh."

"I only asked. Number Two: 'Thou Shalt Not Worship False Gods.' As if I would, for God's sake!"

And I answered, "For My sake you will stop saying things like that. You've just broken My Third Commandment: 'Thou Shalt Not Take The Name Of The Lord Thy God In Vain.' "

And Moses said, "I can see this is going to be more difficult than I thought. I didn't realize You were going to be so picky. So far there are an awful lot of 'Thou shalt nots', isn't there any good news? Oh, this is better, Number Four: 'Remember The Sabbath Day, To Keep It Holy.' That's more like it! At least we get the day off every Saturday."

"No, Moses, every Sunday."

"Sunday? How do you work that out?"

"The first day of the week is Monday, which means the seventh day, the day of rest, is Sunday."

And Moses said, "But us Children of Israel have

45. The Author is referring to Egypt and not to Zebediah's Pyramid Go-Go Bar and Massage Parlour.

always considered Sunday as the start of the week, which gives us Saturday as the day of rest. It's a bit late to start changing it."

And I spake, saying, "Moses, this is a Commandment of the Lord Thy God. I created the Earth and everything that is upon it in six days, Monday to Saturday inclusive, and rested on the seventh, which was Sunday. And so will The Children of Israel."[46]

"All right, I'll do my best but I'm not guaranteeing anything. The Children of Israel don't like people interfering with their social life. Now let's get on, otherwise I'll be here all night.

"Numbers Five and Six: 'Honour Thy Mother And Father' and 'Thou Shalt Not Commit Murder.' Reasonable enough.

"Number Seven: Oh dear, I'm going to have problems with this. You couldn't tone it down could you?"

And I spake, saying, "When I say 'Thou Shalt Not Commit Adultery', I mean 'THOU SHALT NOT COMMIT ADULTERY'."

"Not even occasionally? Say, three times during your life?"

"NO!"

"Be reasonable. We've been doing it ever since You threw Adam and Eve out of the Garden Centre. You told us to go forth and multiply and we couldn't do that without committing adultery."

And I said, "No adultery!"

"Whatever You say. But I'm going to show that clause to Malachi the Lawyer, maybe he can find a loophole."

46. When asked why He allowed The Israelites to defy Him and keep Saturday as The Sabbath, The Author replied, "I'll tell you in Footnote 47."

"There are no loopholes in My Commandments."

"You wait until Malachi starts plea-bargaining on the Murder clause. After listening to him for a few hours, you'll reduce it to Manslaughter, just to get rid of him."[47]

"Moses! I'm tempted to smite thee hip, thigh *and* dangly bits!"

"Enough said! Now, I can't see any problems with Numbers Eight and Nine.[48]

"But this bit in Number Ten, after 'not coveting thy neighbour's ass', telling us we can't covet our neighbour's ox either, that's going to spoil Zebediah's fun.[49]

"Well, if that's the lot, I'll be off to break the bad news to the others."

And I spake, saying, "Thou hast overlooked the P.T.O. on the bottom of the second tablet."

And Moses turned over the tablet and read: "The Eleventh Commandment: 'Thou Shalt Not Turn Thy Sony Walkman Up So Loud That It Annoyeth Others,' What's that supposed to mean?"

And I told him that in the fullness of time, long

47. The Author adds: "I thought I'd have more trouble getting no adultery through, so I traded it in exchange for allowing The Children of Israel to keep Saturday as The Sabbath. Unfortunately, they've been rather more meticulous in taking their day off than they have in obeying Number Seven. Indeed, far too many of them have spent Saturday committing Seven."

48. Commandment Eight is "Thou Shalt Not Steal" and Commandment Nine is "Thou Shalt Not Bear False Witness Against Thy Neighbour." The Author says, "Nine is the Commandment that most people forget, I always compare it to Brad Dexter, the only actor in 'The Magnificent Seven' that most people can't name."

49. Zebediah, ex-proprietor of The Pyramid Go-Go Bar and Massage Parlour, had some *very* strange tastes.

after The Children of Israel had found The Promised Land and called it Florida, there would come a blight of noise boxes which would sin against the ears of others. They would spread across the whole earth like a pestilence of McDonalds franchises, and would be more offensive even than anoraks, musical doorchimes or Care Bears.

And Moses said, "I don't see how this applies to us. So why don't we do a deal: if The Children of Israel solemnly swear never, ever to break this Commandment, will You drop Adultery?"

"No!"

And with that final word I ascended from Sinai, leaving Moses to contemplate My Commandments.[50]

And he spent forty days and forty nights on the mountain. Two in contemplation and the other thirty-eight trying to find his way back.

50. These Commandments have been published in the order The Author dictated them and not in the order in which they are most commonly broken, which, according to The Author is:
    1. Adultery. (7)*
    2. Taking the name of the Lord in vain. (3)
    3. Theft. (8)
    4. Murder. (6)
    5=Having other Gods before Him (1) *and* Worshipping false Gods, particularly television personalities. (2)
    7. Coveting thy neighbour's ass and other parts of his/her anatomy. (10)
    8. Bearing false witness against a neighbour, particularly after he/she has rejected your caressess of his/her ass and other parts of the anatomy. (9)
    9. Not keeping The Sabbath. (4)
    10. Dishonouring mother and/or father. (5)
    The Author adds that His Commandment regarding the Sony Walkman would have shot straight to Number 3 with a bullet had Moses bothered to pass it on.
    (*) Denotes original position in The Top Ten.

The Land Flowing With Milk And Honey

had given My great Commandments to Moses so that he should broadcast them throughout the Earth as the rules by which you anthropoids should live your lives, the basis of all your laws and justice. Through him I had revealed to you the truth of all truths.

And having done this I expected you to abide by My Commandments and dwell for ever in peace so that I could retire and live quietly in Heaven, enjoying My infinite old age untroubled by your petty problems. But if there's no peace for the wicked, there's even less for the perfectly righteous.

Hardly had I put My feet up and started on My ornamental macramé than I got a call from Moses. Serves Me right for forgetting to switch My answering machine on.

"Lord," he said, "I've got a problem."

"Moses," I said, "I am fed up with being a cosmic Agony Aunt, the Automobile Association and a deli, all rolled into one. Go somewhere else with your problem."

"I would, Lord, but this involves both of us. Please, don't ring off until You've heard what I've got to say."

And so, in My infinite patience, I let him speak.

"It's like this: I returned from Sinai to The Children of Israel. And they gathered round me, asking, 'What kept you on the mountain for the past forty days and forty nights?'

"And I said, 'I've been taking a skiing holiday. What do you think kept me? I have been speaking with The Lord and He has vouchsafed me His Commandments which are contained in these tablets of stone.'

"And they said, 'Why are you clutching your groin?'

"And I said, 'Because I've given myself a hernia lugging these bloody great tablets of stone down the mountain.'

"And the Israelites said, 'What are these Commandments?'

"And I recited Your Commandments to them. After I'd finished it went very quiet and so I asked them what they'd been doing while I was away."

"So, Moses," I asked, "what had they been doing?"

"Well, Lord, it seems they'd been having a bit of a party."

"So?"

"So, apparently they had this idea of building a golden calf and celebrating round it and what with the drink, well, one thing led to another and I'm afraid, Lord, that a few things got broken."

"What got broken?"

"At least seven Commandments. Eight, if you include Zedediah and the ox."

So saying, Moses threw himself to the ground and begged My forgiveness, saying "I know they have done wrong and deserve to be punished, but I am pleading with You to spare them. And, in fairness, not one of them broke Your Eleventh Commandment."

And I was moved by his pleas and spake gently unto him saying, "Moses, contrary to what some people believe, I am a Merciful God, and therefore I will not strike down the Israelities with thunderbolts, nor will I rain fire and brimstone upon their heads, nor even turn them into jumbo packs of superior table salt. But they must be punished for transgressing My laws, so I have decided that henceforth the Israelites will carry with them a terrible burden. I will place My Curse on one child in every four. And from this day hence until all eternity every fourth child of the Israelites will be reviled and despised and even his own kith and kin will flee from him, shouting, 'Truly this is the most horrendously boring person we have ever had the misfortune to meet'."

And thus did I place My Curse on the Children of the Children of Israel so that even unto this day, one in four of them is a Chartered Vegetable.[51]

So Moses returned to the Israelites and told them My decision and there was much weeping and wailing

51. The Author adds that, in retrospect, He thinks this punishment might have been too severe, not only to the Israelites and their descendants but also to the rest of us. But He didn't envisage Chartered Accountants becoming as numerous as they are. "I wish I'd told them to go forth and subtract."

and each of them beat their breast and gnashed their gums.[52]

But I hardened My heart against them and to show I meant business I ordained that one in four should immediately become Chartered Vegetables and be put to work conducting a census, counting the number of able-bodied men before they resumed their journey towards The Land Flowing With Milk And Honey.

And Moses reported back to Me when the census was taken, saying that the total number of men was 603,567 and that they were split into thirteen families who became The Thirteen Tribes of Israel. And then Moses said, "Lord, why in Your infinite wisdom, did You make us spend three months counting all 603,567 able-bodied men?"[53]

And I answered, saying, "Merely a whim. Sometimes I just enjoy acting like God."

---

52. Dental hygiene was still in its infancy.

53. For the record the figures broke down thus:
    Tribe of Reuben: 46,500; Tribe of Simeon: 59,300; Tribe of Gad: 45,650; Tribe of Judah: 74,600; Tribe of Issachar: 54,400; Tribe of Zebulun: 57,400; Tribe of Joseph: 40,500; Tribe of Manasseh: 32,200; Tribe of Benjamin: 35,400; Tribe of Dan: 62,700; Tribe of Asher: 41,500; Tribe of Naphtali: 53,400; Tribe of Trevor: 17.

There is no mention in the Old Testament of the 13th and smallest Tribe of Israel, The Tribe of Trevor. The Author explains that Trevor was a close relative of Moses and shared his lack of a sense of direction. When the other tribes set off for The Promised Land, Trevor went in the opposite direction and he and his family were never seen again. They became known as The Lost Tribe of Israel. According to The Author, they wandered aimlessly across the globe for a thousand generations until they finally arrived in The Promised Land in 1979. But due to the exorbitant rents in Miami Beach, they moved on again.

And once more Moses led the 603,567 men and their wives and their children towards The Land Flowing With Milk And Honey. And throughout the journey the 603,567 men and their wives and their children each said, "I think we should go this way" and "No, I'm certain we should go that way" and "I know we've been past this rock at least fifteen times" and "When you've seen one desert, you've seen them all!" and "All I say is, this Land Flowing With Milk And Honey better be something special."

And thus they travelled for forty long and weary years. And as they went each of them wept and wailed and beat their breast. And when they tired of that, they beat Moses's breast and his head and his dangly bits.

At the end of forty years, Moses came to Me and said, "Lord, for forty long and weary years I have led The Children of Israel through the desert and still I cannot find The Land Flowing With Milk and Honey. Tell me where I am going wrong."

And I spake unto Moses, saying, "Moses, for forty years you have been reading the map upside down."

And Moses said, "So where is The Land Flowing With Milk and Honey?"

And I pointed westwards and said, "See that river? That is The Jordan and beyond Jordan is Canaan and that is The Land Flowing With Milk and Honey."

And Moses said, "How far is that from here?"

And I said, "About three hundred yards."

And he said, "Well, I'll be buggered."

And he died.

But before he expired he spake his last words unto Me, saying, "Lord there is something I've always meant to tell You, but could never pluck up my courage to say."

And I said, "Tell Me now Moses."

And he looked at Me and with his dying breath he uttered these words, "You're a lot shorter than I imagined You would be."

So it came to pass that the mantle of Moses passed to Joshua. And after he had let the seams out, raised the hem and had a small alligator embroidered on the breast pocket, he took command.

Thus it was Joshua who finally led The Children of Israel across the River Jordan and into Canaan which was The Land Flowing With Milk and Honey.

And when they arrived there The Children of Israel fell to the ground and kissed the earth. And they raised their heads to the sky and, with one voice cried, "This earth taste like earth. So where's the milk? Where's the honey?"

And I spake with a great voice, saying unto The Children of Israel, "There was milk, there was honey. But research will prove they are packed with cholesterol, so to protect your health I am giving you The Land Flowing With Mineral Water And High-Fibre Bran."

And The Children of Israel set to weeping and wailing and threatening to sue Me for false pretences. And they shrieked, "For forty long and weary years we have journeyed through the desert just for this!" But I ignored them and left them to their misery.

You know, sometimes I really love being Me.

Prophet And Loss

I had achieved all I set out to do. I had created the world in six days, I had populated it and I had finally led My Chosen People into The Land Flowing With Mineral Water And High-Fibre Bran. Having done all this, and tired of being a cosmic au pair to The Children of Israel, I left them to get on with it, while I finally enjoyed a quiet life in Heaven with My macramé. Well, not that quiet because the Children of Israel kept asking Me to pop back to help them out of the various messes they got themselves into. Quite soon after Joshua had assumed leadership, he found himself outside Jericho and didn't know how to take the town. So I told him to march his men round the city while trumpeters blew blasts on their ram horns. Worked a treat.

The Bible says that after the trumpeting the walls just tumbled down. Not quite how it happened.[54]

Whatever their virtues – and the Israelites must have had some, though they don't spring easily to mind – they were not great trumpeters. To be honest – and I can't be anything else – they had no musical ability whatsoever; personally I'd prefer to listen to cats being eviscerated alive than suffer an evening of hearing them murder "Hava Nagila", which was the only tune they knew. And not one of My favourites, I wish I'd made The Twelfth Commandment: "Thou Shalt Not Under Any Circumstances Ever Play, Sing or Otherwise Perform 'Hava Nagila'."[55]

Be that as it may, they started marching around Jericho trumpeting "Hava Nagila" and the Jerichoans – who had an ear for music – were so appalled by the

---

54. The Author adds: "Some of these Old Testament stories should be taken with a pinch of Lot's wife."

55. The Author indicated that He has other Commandments to be passed on including:
• Thou Shalt Not Snigger When Thy Neighbour's Card Is Swallowed By The Cash Dispenser.
• Thou Shalt Not Slam Down The Receiver Before Leaving A Message On Thy Neighbour's Answerphone.
• Thou Shalt Not Covet Thy Neighbour's Parking Space.
He also said He is considering reducing The Deadly Sins to six: "I'm thinking of dropping Sloth as it is unfair to a perfectly harmless, if very boring, animal, which is neither sinful nor deadly. Unless, of course, it happens to fall out of a tree and drop on your head."
    When we questioned Him about this He said, "That's one of My best jokes." He then told us that if we didn't find it funny we should go forth and multiply ourselves, although not exactly in those words.

racket that they started protesting by booing, hissing and throwing rotten greengroceries. When these ran out, they threw whatever else they could lay their hands on, including the bricks in the walls of the city. And so they stupidly demolished their own fortifications.[56]

I felt quite sorry for the Jerichoans, not only were they the cause of their own downfall, they were also rotten shots. Not one brick came anywhere near an Israelite and all the trumpeters lived to play another day. Ultimately, their appalling atonal music influenced such composers as Stockhausen. Although his works never brought the house down.

Between errands like this I kept only a watching brief as the Israelites spent the next centuries squabbling and fighting amongst themselves and with anyone else. The Israelites were their own worst enemies, except, perhaps, for the Philistines and the Romans. They never learned. Look at Samson, would he listen when I advised him that a nice, well-educated Israelite boy should never marry a hairdresser?

And so it went on throughout The Old Testament,

56. It seems the bricks for the walls of Jericho were supplied by the same man who won the contract for The Tower of Babel. After their great victory The Israelites marched in to the ruins of Jericho only to find that several dozen estate agents had got there first and already had outline planning permission to develop the site into a drive-in hyperstore with parking for fifteen hundred chariots.

they ignored My every warning. I kept sending down
My prophets and they just refused to heed them. So in
the end I gave up and scrapped My prophet-sharing
scheme.[57]

57. The Author says He knows this is an old joke – about six
    thousand years old, to be precise – but it still amuses Him.
    And, indeed, it caused the publishers a great deal of mirth.
    When asked His views about modern prophets The Author
    replied: "I am a Merciful God, as I think I may have once
    said, but I find it hard to be patient with those who
    proclaim. 'I have found God!' As though they'd discovered
    Me in a Lost Luggage office like some umbrella carelessly
    left on a train.

    "And I do find it difficult to be Merciful to those who set
    themselves up as My spokesmen on Earth. Never trust
    anyone who says that I speak through them. I am not some
    sort of cosmic ventriloquist. And even if I was, I'd be very
    fussy about up whom I put My hand."

Upstairs, Downstairs

At last I was able to spend more time at home which by now was getting quite full. After so many eons of living alone it was nice to welcome some congenial companions.

As you would expect, we run a pretty tight membership policy. We don't let any old riff-raff in, so it's no good knocking three times on The Pearly Gates and saying, "Come on, Peter, open up! John Paul II sent me and said to give You his regards." We must have a thousand people try that one every day and all are briskly turned away.

We don't, of course, have anything as vulgar as bouncers – not like Downstairs where they have a score of them throwing people in. But nobody gets past St Peter without being sponsored by at least two saints and seconded by a couple of popes.

Not that every pope is a member here. Frankly, I don't know how some of them got the job, especially in the Middle Ages when some very undesirable individuals managed to persuade others that they were My Representative on Earth. The trouble is, I don't have any say in who gets elected as Pope. Now, I'm not saying that John Paul II isn't a good man – he is, even if he does rather overdo the speaking in tongues; making long speeches in a dozen different languages is suspiciously like showing-off – but if I'd had My way I'd have thought twice before electing a pontiff who seems to be unnaturally fond of kissing tarmac.

A strange habit but harmless enough, I suppose, and vastly preferable to the proclivities of some of his predecessors who did not confine their affection to airport runways and seemed to think they had to test every Deadly Sin personally before warning their flock against them. We don't want that sort of person up here and most of them didn't get within a stone's throw of The Pearly Gates – just as well because there's nothing that does a Pearly Gate more damage than having stones thrown at it.[58]

Over the millennia we've tried to keep Heaven

58. When asked to name His favourite pontiffs, The Author said, "There have been 262 of them so it's very difficult to compile My Top of the Popes. For Me, St Peter, who was the very first, is still Number One. But I have trouble remembering some of them. After all, there were fourteen called Clement and twenty-three called John, most confusing, though I'm very fond of John XXIII, who is a charming old chap. But who was Deusdedit? And what possessed one of them to call himself Donus? Sounds like a Turkish kebab." When reminded that St Deusdedit (a.k.a. Adeodatus I) was pope from 615–619 and that Donus held the post from 676–678, The Author told the editor, "Nobody likes a clever Dick."

exclusive. Very few people have even had a glimpse of it, which is probably why so much nonsense has been talked about the place. It's not all fluffy clouds and angels playing harps; there are almost no clouds because most of us like to sunbathe the whole year round and quite a few of the angels now play synthesizers. We move with the times although, as I said to Ludwig only the other day, I vastly prefer "Rock of Ages" to the age of rock![59]

That little *bon mot* amused the dear old chap, who doesn't approve of this new music at all, in fact he recently begged Me to make him deaf again. I think he was joking, although it's difficult to tell with him. He's got a kind heart, though. He spends hours with Schubert suggesting ways in which he might finish his 8th Symphony.

Mozart, on the other hand, has taken to the new technology like a duck to porridge and has written a rock opera called "Cosi Fan Tutti Frutti".[60] Not altogether to My taste; give Me something a little more traditional like "The Hallelujah Chorus" – I'm afraid that even a God as modest as Me likes to hear His name being exalted – but it's very popular with the younger seraphim. Call Me old-fashioned but I do wish they wouldn't wear jeans, even ones with My son's name written on them. No, I may be a fuddy-duddy but I still

59. Ludwig van Beethoven. It would seem The Author is as prone to name-dropping as the rest of us.

60. When we enquired whether The Author means "like a duck to water", He replied, "Do I? I'm sure I designed ducks to live in porridge. Or perhaps I originally intended water to be called porridge and Adam changed the name. I can't see that it's important. I really do wish you wouldn't question every little point."

like to see seraphim dressed in traditional gossamer, at least while they're working.[61]

The nice thing about Heaven, as some of you may find out, although I doubt it, is that it's whatever you want it to be. Everyone has their personal Paradise. My own little bit of Heaven is just a cosy corner which I haven't changed much since I created the place, although Michelangelo did redecorate the ceiling. Very nice too but a bit elaborate. Being a God of simple tastes, I'd have been quite happy with a bit of lining paper and a couple of coats of emulsion. Not that I said anything – you know how temperamental geniuses can be.

Perhaps you don't but that's because you haven't been up here where you can hardly turn round without bumping into one. And, of course, most of you won't have the chance unless you're very, very righteous.

Contrary to popular opinion, the vast majority of you probably won't go Downstairs either. It's possible I've already mentioned that I'm a Merciful God. And as such, I don't like to think of people spending the rest of Eternity in The Other Place unless they really are beyond redemption. I like to believe there's a little good in all of you, so try not to disappoint Me. I make sure that each case is judged carefully and if I feel that a sinner may genuinely repent, I despatch him or her to Limbo.

There are some serious misconceptions about Limbo. Most people seem to think it's like some eternal dentist's waiting room, full of old magazines and dusty

61. According to The Author, gossamer gowns are made by St Michael and available at all Heavenly branches of Marks and Spencer. This may be one of His little jokes. If so, it is undoubtedly very droll.

cacti with some nasty treatment to follow. Not to mention an exorbitantly high bill to pay. (I do apologize for teeth, they are so unreliable. I'll look again at their design when – I mean if – I ever think of scrapping you anthropoids and starting anew.)

Nothing could be farther from the truth. It's a very pleasant place, attractive and comfortable without being opulent. I send people there to mend the errors of their ways, to revitalize their souls and uplift their spirits. It's a bit like a Health Farm with spiritual jacuzzis. After a while the clients emerge looking, feeling and, most important, behaving better and if they've thoroughly cleansed their souls, they may even become probationary members of Heaven. Sadly, though, there are some who won't follow orders and I'm afraid that, with great reluctance, I have to kick them Downstairs.

I won't dwell on The Other Place in detail; if you really want to find out what it's like just try stealing this book.[62]

Suffice to say that it is indescribably vile, filthy, stinking, unbearably hot and crammed with the most loathsome, despicable and genuinely monstrous people. Also the food leaves a lot to be desired. It is a hundred million times worse than the very worst thing you can imagine. Yes, even worse than watching 'The Price is Right' for all eternity.

I keep My visits to a minimum, just popping down to complain when they're being unusually noisy or

62. The Author wishes us to point out that He is much too merciful to impose such a sentence for shop-lifting. But warns that anyone who does try to steal this book is liable to spend the rest of their days in a dentist's waiting room as a cactus.

when they aren't stoking the furnaces sufficiently high and it affects My central heating system.

Otherwise I try to avoid the place because I don't see eye-to-eye with Satan. He's always been an awkward customer. I remember thinking he was a wrong 'un when he was a child and I caught him trying to pull the wings off a cherub.

In those days he was living up here and had he mended his ways he might have done quite well. Some thought he had the makings of an archangel. But his problem was ambition. He got ideas above his station and started thinking he could do better than Me! He used to go around telling the other angels that I was getting too old for the job and trying to tempt them to join him in a boardroom coup against Me.

In the end I had it out with him, face-to-face. I told him that if he didn't change he would regret it.

He said, "Do your worst, you stupid old fool."

And I said, "Satan, being a Merciful God, I don't want to do My worst although I am sorely tempted to."

And he said, "Go on, just this once, give in to temptation."

And I said, "If you think that I would give in to temptation, you can go to Hell."

No sooner had the words left My lips than there was an almightly explosion and he disappeared in a pillar of fire and sulphur. Sometimes I forget My own omnipotence.

He's been in charge of Hell ever since. And when he's not tormenting lost souls, he goes out on recruitment drives, wandering the Earth trying to convince gullible fools to buy a Time Share in Hades.

The End Of
The Word⁶³

I'm drawing towards the end of this little volume of My memoirs. And looking back over all the trials and tribulations of a long and eventful existence, I find I have no regrets. Except, perhaps, that I would have liked to have been taller.

The story isn't complete. It will never be complete because I am Infinite. I have other stories to tell. For example, I have barely touched on My son's story, simply because I have very little to add to what is said in The New Testament.

I also have stories to tell of other life-forms in other

63. When we asked The Author if this was a misprint for "The End Of The World", He waxed wrathful and said, "Why do you question every tiny thing I do? The Lord Thy God does not make typing errors. I am omniscient. If I write 'The End of The Word', I mean it."

worlds in other galaxies in other universes. And some day I may be persuaded to put pen to paper and relate them. Though I'll probably use other publishers. These, if I may be allowed a personal observation, have been unnecessarily over-zealous in questioning some of My facts.[64]

As for My holy ghost writer, well, we finally managed to establish some sort of rapport and he will doubtless spend the rest of his life quite happily as a cactus. In fact, I know he will because I am omniscient.[65]

Omniscience is all very well but it can be a curse. For a start, it ruins My birthday every year because I know in advance what presents I'm going to receive.[66]

Mind you, I'd know that even if I wasn't omniscient because they are the same every year – new pyjamas, a flowing robe and thonged leather sandals – as Gabriel says, "What can you give the God who has everything?"

He says it every year, and I know he's going to say it. And every year I want to say, "Forget about those terrible sandals, why don't you give Me a pair of Reebok trainers?" But I don't.

And every year he says, "Guess what I've made especially for You!"

64. We were going to question the veracity of this statement, but decided against it.

65. The last time we looked, the holy ghost writer seemed quite content on the windowsill and is being well cared for by one of our secretaries. However, we are now faced with the unique problem of paying royalties to a potted plant but our company's Chartered Vegetable is working on it.

66. The Author does not actually have a birthday as He wasn't actually born. However, He holds a celebration on February 30th each year which is a Sunday.

And every year I say, "You've baked Me an archangel cake!"

And every year, he says, "Surprise! Surprise! I've baked You a fruit cake!"

And every year I know he has but I hate to spoil his fun.

And every year he says, "Well, Lord, how old are You this year?"

And every year I say, "Gabriel, I stopped counting after the first thirty-nine millennia."

And every year he says, "I must say You don't look a day over thirty-five thousand!"

And we all laugh.

Then we play a game of "Trivial Pursuit" and every year I win. And every year Gabriel gets grumpy and says, "It's not fair, being omniscient You know all the answers."

And every year I say, "I knew you were going to say that."

And every year he says, "Well, just remember, nobody likes a clever Dick."

And every year I pretend to get cross and say, "Gabriel! You shouldn't talk to the Lord Thy God like that. I've half a mind to send you Downstairs for the rest of eternity."

And every year he says, "But You're not going to."

And every year I say, "Give Me one reason why I won't."

And every year he says, "Because You're a Merciful God."

And every year I say, "Sometimes, Gabriel, I think you're nearly as omniscient as I am."

And we laugh.

MARKS & SPENCER
ST. MICHAEL
SIZE: VAST
VE A GOOD DAY, GOD! HAVE A GOOD DAY, GOD! HAVE A G
PPY BIRTHDAY, GOD! HAPPY BIRTHDAY, GOD
E A HEAVENLY BIRTHDAY, GOD! HAVE A HEAVENLY BIRT

It's the same every year, year in, year out, through infinity. I suppose some of you might think it's boring but it suits Me.

Perhaps omniscience does bring its problems, but I always knew it would so I don't complain. In fact, I complain about very little which is quite remarkable considering how much trouble you anthropoids have caused Me over the millennia.

You're the most disputatious, vexatious and ungrateful of all My creations. Day after day, year after year, century after century you have let Me down. You've gone your own way, ignored My teaching, ridiculed My prophets, abused My priests, waged war and committed atrocity in My name. And I know you'll never change.

Can you wonder that there have been occasions when you've tried even My infinite patience so sorely that I've thought seriously about rubbing you all out and starting again? But call Me sentimental if you like or put it down to the fact that I'm growing mellow in My old age but I haven't yet been so aggravated that I've clicked My fingers and turned you and your little Earth back to the dust from whence I made you.

And perhaps I'm also getting a little bit lazy. Because I start to think, "Why should I go to all the trouble and expend all the energy required to blow them to smithereens when they are quite capable of doing it for themselves? And certainly stupid enough to succeed."

Be assured, one day your microscopic world will disappear. And, being omniscient I know the question you are asking: When will the end of the world come?

I alone know the exact day, hour, minute and second of Armageddon. And I could reveal it here. But

My omniscience shows me the awful effect the news would have on you.

I know the panic, agony and despair that would engulf you. And, in my Infinite wisdom, I have decided to spare you that unbearable anguish.

I also know that if I revealed the date to you, you'd rush straight out to the nearest bookmaker and bet money at enormous odds, certain you'll win a fortune. But, money won't buy you happiness. Indeed, on the day that your bet comes up, it won't buy you anything at all, not even a decent burial.

So I've decided I'm not going to tell you when your world will end. Let's just say that your little Earth, like My story, is to be continued ...

And even though I may have mentioned it in passing before, I am, I think you will agree, a Merciful God.

Amen.

You can get up off your knees now.

In The Beginning ...

n most autobiographies the subject starts at the beginning, but in My case that's tricky. I have no beginning. And for that matter, I have no end. I'm Infinite. So it makes starting the story difficult. Not to mention ending it. In theory this book could continue indefinitely which ... Haven't I written this bit before? That's the trouble with being Infinite, you never know whether something's already happened or is about to happen ...

BY THE SAME AUTHOR

'God On Gardening'

'God Housekeeping – How To Have
a Heavenly Home'

'Kitchen Miracles – Including 101 Ways
To Cook a Quug'

'Build Your Own Universe'

'The Joy Of Begatting' (co-author, The Holy Ghost)

'Begatting, The Do's And Don'ts'

'The Book Of Judgement'
(co-author, The Recording Angel)

'Monroe and Me – My Memories of Marilyn'

INDEX

Figures in *italic* denote illustrations

BIBLEOGRAPHY

In writing this volume The Author occasionally consulted the following sources:

THE BIBLE, Old Testament, various authors including Amos, Daniel, Esther, Ezekiel, Ezra, Habakkuk, Haggai, Hosea, Isaiah, Jeremiah, Job, Joel, Jonah, Joshua, Leviticus, Malachi, Micah, Nahum, Nehemiah, Obadiah, Ruth, Samuel, Zechariah, Zephaniah and Trevor. The latter's work is known as The Lost Book of The Old Testament as Trevor mislaid it somewhere in Canaan during his lifetime's wanderings.

THE BIBLE, New Testament, various authors including Matthew, Mark, Luke, John, Peter, Paul and Mary.

THE RED SEA SCROLLS, the soon-to-be-discovered Book of Trevor. The Author found Chapter 28 – 'From Ur To Thur And Back Again' – particularly misleading.

'THE NOAH LETTERS', written by Noah and his wife Norah to The Author. Also 'The Noah Postcards'. In The Author's own collection.

'ORNAMENTAL MACRAMÉ MADE EASY' by Vera Swain.

ALSO RECOMMENDED

'THE CARE AND PROPAGATION OF CACTI'
by Laurens Wilp

ADDENDA

The following are late additions to The Author's original manuscript.

ANCHOVY
The use of, as a cure for bunions. Apply to affected part. If symptoms still persist, consult a chiropodist.

ANGELS
In an attempt to settle the age-old theological dispute we asked The Author exactly how many angels could stand on a pinhead. He replied, "I am The Lord Thy God and not 'The Guinness Book of Records'."

BUGGROM
A suburb of Sodom, which suffered the same fate.

COCKTAIL ONION
Original inspiration for the planet Dandropy in the thirty-ninth galaxy of the fourth universe, turn left after Nibolt and ask again.

DANDROPY
Don't bother asking directions at Nibolt. Since this book was written Dandropy has ceased to exist.

JEHOVAH'S WITNESSES
The Author requests that they kindly desist from knocking on The Pearly Gates attempting to sell him 'The Watch Tower'.

MABBLE
Small barnacle-like creature found clinging to the bottom of the Ark after it had landed on Mount Ararat. Unable to live outside water and so became instantly extinct.

ORNAMENTAL MACRAMÉ
Since writing the manuscript, The Author has decided that the ornamental macramé hanging basket is a worse plague than boils and wishes every reference to it to be expunged from this work. Unfortunately, His decree came too late to be incorporated into this edition.

SAINT BARRY
Barry Felt will be canonized by Pope Sade in 1997 and created the Patron Saint of Video Producers.

ZYGL
The Author's original name for rubber overshoes.

ERATTA

There are no eratta as The Author does not make mistakes.

ERRATUM

'Eratta' should be spelt 'errata'. The Publisher apologizes for this errer.